Love for Now

Love for Now

Anthony Wilson

IMPRESS BOOKS

First Published 2012
by Impress Books Ltd
Innovation Centre, Rennes Drive, University of Exeter Campus,
Exeter EX4 4RN

Reprinted 2013

© Anthony Wilson 2012

Typeset in 11/13 Sabon by Swales & Willis Ltd, Exeter, Devon

British Library Cataloguing in Publication Data
A catalogue record for this book is available from the British Library

ISBN 13: 978–1–907–60535–2 (paperback)
ISBN 13: 978–1–907–60536–9 (ebook)

Every effort has been made to contact and acknowledge copyright owners,
but the author and publisher would be pleased to have any errors or
omissions brought to their attention so that corrections may be
published at a later printing.

for Tatty
and in memory of Jörn Cann

Contents

Acknowledgements

I am indebted to all the doctors and staff on the Haematology ward where I was treated.

For their friendship, advice and support I would like to thank the first readers of this manuscript: Mark Brend, Mary Jacobs, Zoë Pagnamenta, Victoria Pougatch and Tatiana Wilson.

Grateful acknowledgement is made to the following:

Lines from *Life in a Scotch Sitting Room, Vol. 2*, 'Episode 2', by Ivor Cutler, Rev-Ola Records, 1978.

'How to Behave with the Ill' by Julia Darling, from *What Can I Do to Help? 75 Practical Ideas for Family and Friends from Cancer's Frontline*, Deborah Hutton (ed.), Short Books Ltd © Julia Darling, 2005. Reproduced by permission of Julia Darling's family.

Extracts from *C: Because Cowards Get Cancer Too* by John Diamond, published by Vermilion, reprinted by permission of the Random House Group Ltd.

Lines from 'Death does not come from outside. Death is within' by Jaan Kaplinski, from *Selected Poems*, trans. Fiona Sampson *et al.* (Bloodaxe Books, 2011).

Lines from 'It gets cold in the evening' by Jaan Kaplinski, from *Selected Poems*, trans. the author *et al.* (Bloodaxe Books, 2011).

'Wet Evening in April' by Patrick Kavanagh, from *Collected Poems*, Penguin Classics, 2005.

'A Man Called Percival Lee' by Spike Milligan, from *The One Hundred and One Best and Only Limericks of Spike Milligan*, Penguin Books Ltd, 1988.

Lines from 'I Go Back to May 1937' by Sharon Olds, from *The Gold Cell*, Alfred A. Knopf, Inc., 1987.

'After Frost' from *Grinning Jack* by Brian Patten. Copyright © Brian Patten 1990. Reproduced by permission of the author c/o Rogers, Coleridge & White Ltd., 20 Powis Mews, London W11 1JN.

Extracts from *Lost in Music: A Pop Odyssey* by Giles Smith, Pan Macmillan, London, © Giles Smith, 1995.

Extracts from *Intimations of Mortality* by Violet Weingarten, Alfred A. Knopf, Inc., 1978.

Thanks are due to Rosie Marks, Emily Riall and Samantha Smith for their help with typing this manuscript.

I will always be indebted to the friendship, love and support of my family and friends. In particular I would like to thank Olwen Goodall, Mary and Sidney Jacobs, Ruth and Roger Lewis, Col and Lucy Mallet, Greg Mason, Debra Myhill, Sam and Phil Randall, William Richardson, Lawrence Sail, Jon and Jo Soper, Wendy Tutchings, Dinah Warren, Simon and Kim Wilding, and Liz Wood.

The heroes of this book are the people who were there: my children Merenna and Shimi Wilson, my wife Tatty Wilson and Dr Jörn Cann, whom I was pleased to call my friend.

The chances are, more of us are mortal than have multiple orgasms.

–Violet Weingarten

A man called Percival Lee
Got up one night for a pee
When he got to the loo
It was quarter to two
And when he got back it was three.

–Spike Milligan

I want to live.

–Sharon Olds

Introduction

I was formally diagnosed with a variant of non-Hodgkin's lymphoma, a cancer of the lymphatic system, on Valentine's Day, 2006. I was 42.

Despite my friends' protestations that it was 'probably nothing', the diagnosis, when it finally came, was not a surprise. A shock, yes; a surprise, no. Just as the treatment for cancer changes your tastebuds, it also heightens your need for the truth.

I looked for the truth about cancer in many different places. Like a good patient I read up on my disease, seeing it as homework. I quickly gave up. What difference did it make how much knowledge I had of the mutating cells in my body? However much knowledge I gained about them would never change their behaviour.

Some of the least satisfying sources of truth about cancer are the media. Coming to terms with a life-changing diagnosis is hard enough, but it is harder when the story you are living through and trying to make sense of also exists in a parallel universe of cancer as portrayed in the lives of celebrities, soap operas and sports personalities. It goes without saying that however frank these representations pertain to be, they ultimately fall short of one's own lived experience. Therefore, the risk inherent in writing this book is that, however accurate its portrayal of cancer and its treatment, it will fall short of the reader's own experience. Every one of us whose lives have been touched by the disease has a unique story to tell.

All I have attempted to do with my own story is to tell it as accurately as possible.

As my treatment for cancer progressed, I became sensitised to its depiction in the culture at large. In particular I was struck by the use of the metaphor of war to describe individuals' experience of the disease, often written or spoken in the past tense: 'X has died today, after a short/long battle with cancer'. If there is one difference I wish to make with this book, it is to challenge the use of such metaphor as the predominant discourse of cancer in our culture.

Speaking personally, describing cancer as a 'battle' or 'fight' places the onus of recovery onto the patient when they are at their most vulnerable. Not one of my fellow-patients and friends who have been diagnosed with cancer has perceived themselves as fighting this battle. If it is a battle, let it be one for the doctors and researchers, who can at least go home in the evening without throwing up their lunch.

Secondly, war metaphor unnecessarily romanticises cancer. The past tense so often used to describe individuals' 'battles' is a tacit reminder that the battle has been lost. None of us like to think we are on the losing side, especially when it comes to the ultimate question of death. Describing cancer as a 'battle' is something of a protective device, therefore: we can live with the loss of a loved one because we can persuade ourselves that 'they gave it everything' before they died.

The truth about cancer is less likely to appear between the pages of a glossy magazine, in the teary recollections of those we invite into our homes at the flick of a television or radio switch, nearly always after the event and by necessity somewhat airbrushed. It is more likely to be found in the unexpected acts of kindness one encounters; the visits and gifts of colleagues and friends; the humour of doctors at moments of crisis; the simple everyday gift of family life continuing around you. In my view, and with one or two honourable exceptions, these are not remarked on in the literature of cancer with anything like enough frequency.

The story related here, is, therefore, my attempt to be true to the experience of living with cancer. If you are reading this there is a fairly good chance you are doing so because you have cancer yourself or know someone who has. My story is not going to be the same as your story, nor that of your friend or relative. But in saying what happened to me, and relating as precisely as possible the words that were said to me, in the order that they were uttered, I hope they create a space in which the reader's own experience, however different, can be reflected upon and spoken of with those the reader knows and loves most closely. I began writing this book in an effort not to forget what I was going through; as the writing progressed it became a debt of honour, to my family and friends, and to the doctors and nurses who treated me. I hope that reading this book will provoke conversation between those who experience cancer directly or in the lives of loved ones. I would argue that we remain uncomfortable about doing that in our culture, the evidence of which can be seen in our over-reliance on metaphors of war to describe experience of the disease. In such a technologically advanced age, this is surely a very great irony. Only by speaking about our experiences honestly, without resort to such symbolism, will we say how it really is. To do that, we need to start with the events as they occurred.

Anthony Wilson
Exeter, March 2012

Prelude

August, 2005

'Dad?'

We are on the M6, in bright sunshine, driving home from our summer holiday in the Scottish Borders. An old Smiths compilation is going full blast as our campervan is overtaken by a juggernaut. At the very point that its slipstream sends us swaying almost into another lane, Morrissey can be heard extolling the virtues of meeting his death under the wheels of a double-decker bus. The irony is not lost on me, and my fists pound the steering wheel with pleasure.

'*Dad*?'

'What? Sorry. What?'

Merenna, my daughter, has crawled across piles of luggage and twisted herself round to face the direction we are travelling, resting her head between the two front seats.

'Dad, when we get home, can I burn this CD off you?'

In a few weeks Merenna will start a new life, at secondary school.

Our holiday has also been one of transitions: music has blared from bedrooms, appearances at breakfast have been silent, or rare. Family walks, always something of a battleground, have still been undertaken, but now we stretch across hillsides in an unruly line, where once we marched in a clump, holding hands.

'So, Dad, can I?'

I still regard seeing the Smiths at the ICA in October 1983 as one of the most formative experiences of my life. Though I heard it only once, I sang 'Reel Around The Fountain' under my breath for the whole of the next week. When I first went out with the woman who is now sitting next to me I pretty much knew the instant she said her favourite song of theirs was 'There Is A Light That Never Goes Out' that we would get married.

So when my daughter, recently awake on a motorway,

expresses interest in the band I fell in love to and with, something hard-wired in my DNA shouts 'Yes!' at the windscreen and punches the steering wheel a little bit harder.

I do none of this, of course.

'What, the Smiths, of course you can my darling. Any time you want.'

From even further back in the van my son Shimi asks if he can borrow it, too. Tatty and I exchange glances. She knows how pleased this has made me, and how hard I am working to feign nonchalance.

Seven hours later we stumble across the threshold of our house in Exeter, the doormat a choppy ocean of mail. Among the usual bills and postcards of holidays from friends there is a letter from Peter Carpenter, my editor at Worple Press in Kent. It tells me he has decided to take *Full Stretch*, my next book of poems, and what what's more, he is going to add selections of my previous books, now out of print, to the new work. 'It'll be a bumper edition,' he says, 'and we've pencilled it for the spring.'

Much later still, our bags unpacked, Tatty says into the darkness 'What was the best bit of your holiday?' This is one of our rituals. We ask the same question of each other every summer, however the holiday has gone. For once it does not take me unawares.

'Was it getting your book contract?'

'No. It was the kids asking to burn the Smiths off me. I feel I've finally arrived as a parent. Whatever else happens, at least I've passed on that.'

Diagnosis

7 February, 2006

Is there a moment when you know?

From my ultrasound to my biopsy took just 11 days. It was when the scan-doctor said I would need a CT scan in two weeks and they made an appointment the same evening for me to have one 48 hours later that I really got worried. The CT was a Thursday. They said 'You'll know the results in two weeks,' but my GP phoned the next morning, asking to see me. This was even worse.

Tatty took that day off, so we could see him together. He said 'If this abnormality hadn't been pressing on your urethra and therefore giving you pain, we may never have known about it. It's a blessing, really.' He confirmed that it was indeed solid – not a polyp or a cyst – and on my lymph nodes. I asked him directly if there was a possibility that it was lymphoma and for the first time he looked away slightly before saying that yes, he couldn't rule that possibility out.

I'm at home now, propped up on the bed. Officially I won't know for sure for another 10/12 days. But right there, in the GP's face, and in the way he reached for an envelope to send my notes in with me to hospital, there was a tensing and a reluctance and a pursing of the lips. The merest hint of a nod.

And that was when I knew.

At the same time, I know nothing of course. All to play for. Not even half-time. Plenty left in the tank. 'It might be completely benign, probably is, you know,' as a friend said on the weekend. (This is well-meaning, but bollocks, intended to reassure them more than me.)

The first discussion with the senior staff registrar at the Emergency Medical Unit said it all too, but in a different way. Her name is Esther. She is smiley, hair up at the back, glasses, the trace of a Northern-Irish or Northern-Irish-Scots accent. She has pink chubby fingers and puts her hands out to touch me a lot on my forearm and my shoulder. She began by asking me what I knew.

She stopped me, two words in, when I said 'tumour'. 'Well, we don't know that, just yet. I think we have to say "abnormality" for now. We must do, until we know more.' 'Right, well, this abnormality, then, is on my,' I paused, looking at her for reassurance. She nodded, knowing I was going to say 'lymph nodes'. 'And it's pressing on my kidneys. Hence the pain.'

She beamed. 'That's right, yes. It's actually the tube coming out of your kidneys, your urethra, but, yes, that's why you're in pain.'

Tatty said, 'And it is solid, isn't it?'

We had been told to ask this by a medical friend. Liquid usually means safe; solid means bad.

The smile fell from her face.

'Yes, as far as we can tell it is, yes.'

She smiled again. 'But, for now, we'll run a few tests, then go from there.' She touched my arm.

'Is that alright?'

'Of course, absolutely.'

'In a minute I'll have to examine you. I hope you don't mind me asking, but has your GP mentioned your testicles at all?'

Tatty and I glanced at each other. It's long been a private joke between us that whenever I go to the doctor's, it's always my balls they end up looking at. I've had this feeling since I was six.

'Well, he did, yes, actually.'

Tatty's hand was gripping mine strongly. I knew if I looked across at her I'd get what she calls church-giggles.

'He had a little look as well. He said they were fine.'

'Good. Delighted to hear it.'

Later, after inviting Tatty to step outside the curtain, she did examine them.

She looked up from them grinning confidently.

'Your GP was right. They're fine.'

'Phew,' was all I could think of to say. 'But do you mind me asking, I mean, why, now, I mean, if this thing in my tummy is there,' I pointed at my stomach, 'what's it got to do with my b..., I mean, my testicles?'

'Well, Mr Wilson, we're trying to go down a diagnostic path here, and the first thing to rule out is the possibility that your lymph nodes have swollen to fight off something elsewhere in your body. And the most likely thing, in a man your age, is that it could be testicular cancer.'

She saw me frown and stopped.

'So although it's in here, it could be down there?'

I was doing a lot of pointing again.

'Yes, but don't worry. In a man your age and in good health like you, testicular cancer really is treatable you know. It's the one to have.'

'Rock on,' I said.

It made her laugh, and Tatty, too.

'And how will you know if it is or not?'

'We'll do that tomorrow I think. I'm going to book you for an ultrasound scan first thing in the morning.'

'On my testicles?'

'On your testicles.'

'Great. Good. I mean, thank you.'

'In the meantime, I'll do my Dracula bit,' she tapped the tray of waiting syringes, 'then you'll be free to go.'

8 February

The ultrasound man wore chinos and a pale green Lee Cooper shirt. Salt and pepper hair, nice smile. They have such a wrapt, alert look of concentration when they look at the screen. It's close to a look of wonder, part-frown, mouth slightly open. He found nothing in my balls. On the way back to the ward Tatty said their insides had looked like lychees.

Like every doctor so far he had got me to tell the story back to him. When I got to the part about it being difficult to biopsy through my back, hence 'looking for more, er, accessible material,' he interrupted, with a rather gruff, 'Not for us, it isn't.'

When Esther came over to explain he'd found nothing we inevitably probed her with more questions. She did likewise.

'Mr Wilson, you remember when I asked you about your alcohol consumption I asked if you ever felt nauseous with it?'

'Yes? I mean, yes I do. I mean, I do remember and don't feel nauseous. Why?'

'It's one of the symptoms, that's all.'

'One of the symptoms of what?'

'One of the symptoms of lymphoma.'

'Which means you now think that's what it is?'

'We don't think it *is*, but we need to test you to rule it out.'

'A biopsy through the back?'

'Yes.'

She began again: 'And night sweats, do you get those at all?'

'Another symptom? No, I don't.'

'We just have to go down the path I'm afraid. Of asking you everything. In case it is. Which we hope it isn't.'

And then I couldn't help myself.

'Why does the lymph system do this? I mean, make growths, abnormalities, whatever we want to call them, when it's the system that's supposed to protect you?'

For the first time she looked upset, the guard dropping a little. She waved her hands in front of her hair, gave a tense smile and briefly caught a glance at the ceiling.

She tried to breathe a chuckle.

'We. We don't know, Mr Wilson, to be honest. It's one of the big questions. What we do know is that for some reason your body has made one and that we need to sort it out for you.'

10

'I'm sorry. Thank you.'

'No, it's fine, you must ask if you need to.'

'Usually it works like this.' She perched on the end of the bed. 'The body has different sites of lymph nodes, where I examined you yesterday, if you remember. When you've an infection or some disease the body needs to fight off, these are what makes the body resist it. And sometimes,' she patted my arm, 'the cells which do that go on growing once the infection is over. And that seems to be what's happened in your case.' She scanned my face and tried on a smile. 'We don't know why it happens.'

'So when you biopsy me, that's what you'll be looking for?'

'Yes, it is.'

The biopsy was not a quick procedure. The radiologist kept emphasising how I'd need to keep absolutely still while they were taking the plugs of material from me because he was using 'the biggest needle I've got.'

'Will I feel anything?'

'No. We'll jab you first with a local.'

'Good. Which way will you go in?'

'Through your back I should think. There are too many organs in the front to get in the way. Your small intestine. One of your main arteries. That sort of thing.'

'Oh.'

'And even going through your back we've only a fine margin of error. So keep as still as you can and we'll be fine.' He reached out to pat my shoulder.

I lay on the ironing board on my stomach, and waited.

They were just about to press the green light when they stopped. 'Mr Wilson, you can sit up if you like,' the nurse said. 'Doctor's gone out for a chat about which is the best way.'

I sat on the ironing board in my gown, my uncovered back now feeling cold. I looked down at my feet and was surprised to see I'd kept my socks on, a pair of woolly ones my grandmother once knitted me.

11

'What's going on?' I asked.

'We don't really know. They're talking, it looks like, about whether it's through your tummy or not.'

'Oh, I thought they'd decided.'

'Well, they had. Now they're talking about it.'

The doctor came back in.

'Nothing to worry about Mr Wilson. It *is* the back, as we've said all along. My colleagues needed to, er, talk it through with me.'

He was standing in front of me, clearly keen to get on with it.

'So if you'll resume your position, if you could, that will be great.'

This time they inserted some bedding, a towel or something, just above my knees and ankles. It made a huge difference. I felt my body go limp. Under my cheek they slotted a large sponge, with a paper towel covering it, I guessed to catch my saliva. Another nurse came round to the other side of the polo, where my head would soon be sticking out.

'Nice and still now, Mr Wilson, if you would, nice and still from now on,' I heard from above. I began to slide into the machine. 'First injection coming now, Mr Wilson. This will give us the image from which we'll work.'

I prayed I wouldn't shit myself.

'That's lovely, Mr Wilson, you're doing great.'

The machine slid me back to where I had come from.

'Now, I'm just going to start prepping your back. Bit cold where I'm rubbing you' – it was cold – 'and in a minute a couple of sharp scratches.'

I had made the decision to turn away from the main action as soon as I lay down. My hands were joined above my head, just above the paper-covered sponge. I felt someone else's fingers interlock with mine. It was the nurse. She began to ask me what I did. I grunted. 'I train teachers. Primary School ones. You know, at Luke's.'

'Oh, Luke's,' she said. 'My daughter wants to do Early Years at Rolle. Well, Plymouth.'

'Good for her.'

'How long you done that then?'

'Three and a half years.'

'Like it?'

'Love it. I miss it, actually.'

'I'm not surprised, love.' She squeezed my fingers.

I heard a tap gushing, the sound of hands greasing themselves with soap.

'OK Mr Wilson, some scratches now. It's the local, in order that we can proceed.'

'Fine.'

'I'm just getting my felt tip out a minute, X marks the spot kind of thing, then we'll get going.'

'Fine.' He drew on my back.

'Here come the scratches, Mr Wilson.'

'Fire away.'

'D'you feel that?'

'Yes. A bit. It's OK.'

'You're doing very well. Here comes the other.'

This was much worse. I felt my whole body wince with the pain. The hands from above kneaded mine.

'I say, Mr Wilson. You're doing very well. It should take effect soon. Can you feel that?'

He prodded my back.

'No not really. Just the pressure of your thumb.'

'OK. That's great. You really are doing extremely well. Nice and still now while we go in. Did you feel anything there?'

'Nothing at all.'

The fingers kneaded.

'And now?'

'No.'

'Great. Just keep it like this and we'll be done in no time. We're going to send you in again with another shot into your cannula. Then we'll take out the material.'

Once again the warm jet into my hand. The polo whirred. The hands had disappeared. 'Take a deep breath. And. Breathe away.'

I reversed back out of the polo.

'We've taken our photo Mr Wilson. In a second you'll hear some loud clicks. That's me taking the material. It won't hurt.'

'Good.'

The click was very loud. 'OK. Nice and still, you're doing extremely well, here comes click two.'

The hands were back, stroking my fingers up and down.

'And, just to be sure, we'll take one more, here it comes now.'

Click!

And that was it.

'Brilliant, Mr Wilson, you did absolutely wonderfully well. Really well done. Nice and still for one minute more while we tidy you up.'

I felt them wiping me with what felt like a small sponge.

'Nearly done there Mr Wilson,' said the nurse.

'Is the needle out?' I asked.

'Oh yes, ages ago. Now we're just making you comfortable. In a minute you can sit up.'

The doors to the CT room burst open. A bed was wheeled in and parked next to the ironing board. A foot started pumping somewhere below the bed and magically it came to rest level with me.

'So, Mr Wilson, really well done, we're going to ask you to lift yourself up off the bed and walk your legs across to the bed next to you.'

I felt my legs obey, but my body was not so compliant. Two pairs of arms reached under mine and gently levered me up. I pushed down on the ironing board and slid myself over onto the bed. I looked back at where I'd been lying and was just in time to see a large smear of blood being mopped up.

'Just a little bleeding,' the doctor smiled. 'Really nothing to worry about.'

And then I felt myself being wheeled back through the doors, across the radiology corridor, and into a small bay off it, next to two empty beds.

Tatty was there waiting for me. She bent down and kissed my forehead. 'I'm so proud of you.'

My doctor came over and smiled at me from his great height. 'Well, we hope we got enough material. Sometimes it's just dead cells. We certainly hope not.'

I smiled back, feeling suddenly sore.

For the first time I knew I was scared.

Groggy from the biopsy, and in a little room off the main ward, Tatty brought me a fantastic apricot and custard Danish from the hospital 'boulangerie' with a coffee. But I was forbidden to sit up to drink or eat.

Esther appeared in my doorway and asked how it went.

'First it was through my back, then through my tummy, then my back again. Apparently there were three of them there behind the screen deciding which way to go. It's obviously not easy to get to.'

I took another mouthful of Danish.

Tatty said, 'He'll be hating this. Crumbs in bed drive him mad.'

Esther found this hilarious.

'Do you want a bit?' I said.

'I think you deserve it far more than me.'

'Tatty's right. I do hate crumbs. But it's an amazing Danish. Anyway they got three plugs of stuff in the end. The only thing was, he told me he couldn't be 100% sure they got enough because of the obliqueness of the angle they had to use. He said they might have got only dead cells, but was hopeful they had enough.'

'This sometimes happens,' she said.

She looked down at my hopeless attempts to sip coffee through the lid of my cup.

'It looks like you need a straw. Straws I can do.' And she left.

I saw James Bradley for coffee today. He came round half one-ish, just as I finished the kitchen floor.

After the usual banter (Palace lost to Preston in the Cup), we got down to brass tacks. He told me that what happens to the lymph gland is it starts splitting cells – or rather, cells start splitting within it, and this forms a solid mass. Like Dr Esther, he has no idea why this happens.

'How close is it to the aorta?'

'Very.'

He frowned.

'Of course that might not be tricky, the aorta, even though it's like a hosepipe,' he made an 'O' with his fingers, 'is extremely flexible. They'll probably hold it out of the way while they work on the lump.'

'You're talking about surgery?'

'Even if it isn't malign, they'll still have to get rid of it, surely,' he said, matter-of-factly.

'The good news is,' he brightened, 'it doesn't sound aggressive. No signs anywhere else?'

'None.'

'They might not even need to use chemo then.'

He's such a delight, even though his brain does move so fast. He brought me McGough's new Penguin *Selected*, just about the perfect gift for 'raising a smile' as he put it.

'I knew Birkett of Birkett's Lymphoma fame,' he told me. 'Friend of mine at Cambridge. You can see his statue at Dublin airport in a line of famous Irish scientists.'

9 February

Not a bad night last night. Don't remember waking or sweating. The first night back after hospital was dreadful, waking drenched with sweat and hardly sleeping at all. It took me back to Esther's methodical questioning. The next night was also sweaty, but less so. Let's hope it was nothing. It reminded me of Thom Gunn's poem. I swear I lay awake planning and saying over to myself lines of seven syllables in homage to him: 'On re-reading "The Man with Night Sweats"', daft and somehow grand. I'm sure there was even a line there which rhymed 'plague' and 'gay'. Not clever.

I've hardly been able to read anything. Hardly any poetry. I just don't seem to want it. All I have read is the sports pages, and little bits of Jaan Kaplinski:

> Death does not come from outside. Death is within.
> …
> Makes with us our first sexual contacts.
> Marries, bears children, quarrels, makes up.
> Separates, or perhaps not, with us.
> Goes to work, goes to the doctor, goes camping,
> To the convalescent home and the sanatorium.

Bizarrely, I find this reassuring, because it is simple and not trying to 'say' anything. Almost refreshing in his way, and also because so little of nearly everything spends its time in the circle of the final questions. And he is not afraid to do that – like Carver and Tranströmer, who I also go back to most often. As always, I think when I read him: 'How does he know so much about *me*?'

Dictionaries are useless. Under lymphoma it first says 'tumour of the lymphatic system'. Under 'tumour' (I even know what that is!) it says 'morbid growth'; and under 'morbid' all it says is 'of death, disease'. A diseased growth on my lymphatic nodes, well I knew that. Why doesn't my dictionary say 'Anthony you have cancer of the lymphatic system'? I did learn that lymph is pale yellow, apparently, and alkaline, and slightly salty to the taste. Good. I wouldn't want it to be green and acid and tasting of bile, because that would be really scary.

Saturday 11 February

They told me yesterday.

I saw Alison (a GP) at the school gates with Juliette. As with the others earlier in the week she insisted not having heard was a good sign. I replied I knew it was still a week before they said they'd ring me, but couldn't dislodge the need to know, nevertheless. Earlier in the week Jasper Hampson had said to me in the street: 'But if it was good news, why would they delay telling you? It's completely illogical.' So I bought Shimi a cake and gave him tea, and once he was ensconced on the computer, called Esther at EMU.

The secretary was efficient, calm. 'Does she know you?'

I could hear her passing the phone, asking if she needed my notes. I could hear Esther saying No, she wouldn't.

'Hello, Esther, I just had one quick question if that's okay?'

'Mr Wilson. You've saved me a phone call actually. I was going to call you later.'

'Well, shall I ask my question? You might be answering it anyway, in a minute, if you know what I mean.'

'Fire away.'

'Well, I was first wondering, does not having heard anything mean anything one way or the other, I mean, I know you said two weeks.'

'It's academic now, in any case. We've had your results. It is lymphoma, as we had thought.'

There was a silence.

'Well thank you for letting me know. That's good. I mean, it's not good, it's good of you to tell me. Thank you.'

'Do you have a pen? I need to give you some details about next week, who you're going to see next.'

'Yes, right, a pen. Thank you.'

Then she told me I was going to see a consultant haematologist, on Tuesday, in area A, Level 1, at 9.30.

'Thank you for everything.'

'That's alright. Goodbye.'

A great blankness came over me as I pressed the red button on the phone. I went to the window overlooking the road and thinking (not at all over-dramatically, I thought): How many more times will I witness this perfectly ordinary scene of people walking back from school, parking their cars and standing talking on the pavement? Then I took another circuit of the room and wondered why I did not feel more anguished. I almost said out loud 'What am I supposed to do now?' I plonked myself back down on the sofa, picked up the *Guardian* I'd been reading five minutes before, and continued scanning the album reviews, as if I'd just put the phone down to my mother. As it happens, I'm not really bothered what the *Guardian* (or anyone else) thinks about the new Miles Davis outtakes box-set, as it is music not aimed at me, and he doesn't need me to help him. But at that moment it took on a vital new significance, What the *Guardian* Thinks Of The New Miles Davis Outtakes Box-Set, as if it had become part of my new and as yet unsaid resistance to having cancer. I cannot remember a syllable of that article. But I do know that the sun came out, briefly, that a car went on being parked, that the house made its usual ticking noises, and that I felt utterly empty, nonplussed, lost in thought and completely thought-less at the same time.

I went and stood by the other window, then sat on the bed for a few pages of *The Stone Diaries* until I heard Tatty's key in the door. I haven't picked it up since.

Later I phoned round the family. Both Mummy and Daddy said, 'I'm so sorry.' Mummy cried quite a lot. 'We love you, darling.'

When I phoned Mart he went even quieter than normal (I can hardly hear him on the phone these days). 'I'm sorry, Ant.' Rich said, when I told him it was lymphoma, 'Wow! Ant! What is it? How are you feeling?' And Sarah, back at Grove Road, having heard it all on speaker phone, said she was sorry too, and maybe they could come down sometime soon.

Then I went to Robyn and Rory, and the Olsens. All I remember is what they were eating. The Laceys some kind of vegetable broth, with dumplings, all five of them seated round their tiny square table like that Van Gough picture of the potato eaters. Robyn put her arm round me. 'It's not the end, Ant. Look at me. I'm still here. You've just got to write off a year of your life and get better.'

Adam had three flat fish all ready for the oven: 'Two Dover Sole and one fat Brill.'

'I love Brill,' I said. Since his cooking course he's obviously going for it, the table full of plates with chopped veg and ingredients. Military planning in his mises. They gave me hugs and said if there was anything they could do, anything, and I said we certainly would. The main thing is that none of them text Bendy, in Germany on her school trip. We have to tell her face to face.

She's already called three times. She could be in Basingstoke, for all the going outside she has done. Apparently she woke up at Dover and said Hooray, we're in France. 'The white cliffs of Dover are in England you dur,' she was told. The highlight was the breakfast in Calais. 'Then I slept through Belgium and the Netherlands.'

'You didn't miss much,' I said.

She rang this morning, from a shopping trip in a German mall, and spent the time discussing the insides of the Kinder egg I had originally bought for Shim.

We told Shimi pretty quickly. As he said two weeks ago, when we said I might have cancer, his first response was 'Are you going to die?' and then, 'Do you feel better now you know?' He always gets to the point. Two minutes later he was on MSN to Louis. 'My dad has cancer.' Louis replied 'I am so sorry. How are you feeling?' Not bad for a ten-year-old boy. Stored during all the phone calls to family there was a teary message from Maura re Louis's MSN message. 'Is it true? I only saw Anthony at 3 o'clock and he had no news at that stage.' I phoned her back and she told me how loved I was, and brave, and how the Eric James book she's lent me really is full of the most wonderful applied theology. 'And I will continually hold you in the light, I promise.'

This was both comfort and accusation. Dipping in at random I found a beautiful and learned passage on the suffering of King Lear. Just my thing. But the words swam in front of me. I feel I am reduced to reading like a teenager, only able to sustain interest and concentration if the words are actually about me. I threw it across the room, where it has stayed. One day I might be able to confess this to Maura.

The worst moment was when Tatty walked in from work. I had put the phone down five minutes before. 'Hi, darling. I'm absolutely feeling dreadful. I think it's flu.' And the thing I nearly said, but didn't, was 'You feel bad? I've just been told I've got cancer.' I let her go on for a bit, then she said 'Did you call them?' And I told her. We stood for a long time hugging each other in the hall, not saying very much. I stroked her head and whispered 'Sorry' into her neck.

13 February

I managed a bike ride into town with Shimi yesterday, to take back CDs, then we went round the quay and stopped off for a smoothie and a bun at Mango's.

He was intensely interested in a man driving a council roadsweeper, a miniature one, with brushes rotating at the front to sweep up the litter. The man, dressed entirely in luminous clothing, took a long time finding the right key to unlock a bin by the riverside. We watched him putting in a new plastic bag and tie up the full one onto the back of the roadsweeper.

Then suddenly: 'Are you going to lose your hair, Dad?' It was the first thing he had said on the night we told him, before asking if we would be poor.

'Haven't got much to lose anyway,' I said.

'Can we go now, Dad?'

'Yup, let's go and pay.'

Merenna gets home tonight. Since going off to Germany the main thing we've said to people is not to text or ring the mobile as she needs to know from us first. Poor girl, she'll get here, exhausted and probably ill, at midnight, to be told her dad has cancer.

On Friday I was all for telling everyone, with the proviso they didn't get in touch, but how can you do that? It's gone against the grain, but it has been the right thing to do. Bendy must come first. She has to hear from us. And anyway, it's not till Tuesday that we will know more ourselves, so perhaps it's just as well. This way we can at least say on Tuesday afternoon that it's x variety at y stage, and is treatable by z. So the phone hasn't been ringing wildly all weekend (what bliss) but I know all of that is about to change.

I have used having cancer as an excuse for some retail therapy on Amazon. It makes you realise life is too short to go without Grover Washington in the kitchen on CD, when you only play the LP on special occasions in the sitting room.

I have re-bought the following:

Grover Washington Junior: *Mister Magic*
Talking Heads: *Remain in Light*
Nick Drake: *Way to Blue*
The Vulgar Boatmen: *Opposite Sex*
Harold Budd: *The Serpent in Quicksilver*
and Everything But The Girl's *Acoustic*.

Why live without what you know will make you happy? The thing is, I can see myself needing a lot more therapy soon. It's addictive, the one-click business, and so easy; I'm going for the *Best Of the Go-Betweens* and some of those late Talk Talk LPs Tatty winces at.

It's also made me track down all the Van and Cocteaus and Blue Nile CDs I've been too lazy to listen to all this time. It turns out I own far more Van Morrison than is actually legal. This week alone I've been reacquainted with *Hard Nose the Highway*, *No Guru, No Teacher, No Method*, *Into the Music*, *Common One* and *Irish Heartbeat*. I've genuinely had pleasure from them all, especially *Common One*, which seems (sorry) seamless, a whole, a complete *work*, as Mart would say, and *Into the Music*, the last three tracks particularly. There's a moment on 'And the Healing Has Begun' when he yells at his band with an instruction, and he gives a little yelp as he does it, the piano taking a lovely fill at the top of the keyboard, a signal that he intends his musicians to Go For It Or Else that is somehow bossy, sexy, gorgeous and hilarious all at once. It's one of my favourite moments in music, and I bet he rehearsed them raw to get there.

Rich was good on the phone on Saturday. We talked about the England v. Italy rugby game and cancer, in that order.

He asked me, 'What's it like telling people?'

Good question. 'Not easy. I find I just go in and say it.' Like I've been doing it all my life.

'How do they react?'

'Well, quite a lot of "Oh I'm so sorry", but I've also had two "Oh shits."'

'You could do a survey.'

'A research project. Fantastic idea. Work would be proud.'

Mummy and Daddy on the phone a minute ago. A local doctor friend of theirs has told them: 'Anthony is the same Anthony he was before. He hasn't changed.'

'Haven't I?' I said.

'Well, no, you have, I mean you have this thing inside you we wish wasn't there, but you're still you, you're the you you were before we knew, that's what she was saying.'

'Right, I see,' not seeing at all.

15 February

We went to see the consultant yesterday, walking hand in hand. A bright, dazzling day, too bright, actually, to look into the light, or even lift your head up from the pavement.

My consultant has twinkly eyes behind little steel-rimmed specs, and discretely expensive clothing. Her name is Felicity Carr. I addressed her from the off as Felicity.

I saw her before I met her formally, as they were taking my blood. In the bloods room a woman in a white coat sat in front of a computer next to which sat an enormous machine like an overgrown breadmaker. She poked her head around the door beaming and cradling a blue mug of coffee. 'You must be my new young gentleman,' she said. 'I'll be seeing you in a minute.'

'I'm sorry to have to see you like this, under these circumstances,' she began, ushering us into the chairs behind her broad desk. Her hand moved across to a dictaphone and clicked it to 'ON'. 'Tell me your story, why you're here.'

So I told her, eventually running out of words, through nerves, at the bit about my biopsy, as if it isn't still fresh in my mind. Thank God for Tatty being there.

She is charming, but very direct. The most difficult moment occurred just as Janette, the specialist Haematology nurse, joined us. Felicity turned to explain to her: 'This is my new young gentleman, Anthony Wilson, he has a high-grade lymphoma.'

'I'm sorry, what did you say, was it "high-grade"?'

'Yes, I'm sorry, I haven't explained. It means active, aggressive actually.'

This had the effect of moving the conversation on rapidly. She had said it was non-Hodgkin's lymphoma, and that, yes, it was a cancer, but that it was highly treatable, with a more than 83% success rate. Funnily enough, she said, Exeter was a bit of a hot spot for it, with 40–50 cases last year. I was going to have the opportunity to be part of a trial if I wanted, in my treatment.

'So does that mean it's bad?'

'Well, actually, paradoxically, it means it's easier to treat.'

'Because?'

'Because the low-grade or indolent variety are common to people older than yourself and they can last for years.'

'Right.'

'And you have B-cell, not T-cell, lymphoma, which, let me assure you, is much better.'

'Good. But it is aggressive?'

'Yes. Which means – I'm sorry – we are going to need to start treating you straight away. I'm afraid it's going to be quite tough going for you for a while.' She blinked, once. By this time I was fiddling with my wedding ring, my default nervous reaction, and I dropped it. And that's when I felt the urge to cry, except I was trying to pick up my ring while holding eye contact.

I needn't have worried. Tatty had got there first. There was a lot of searching for tissues, with Janette having to leave us eventually for a box she perched on the corner of the desk in front of her.

'I'm sorry,' said Dr Carr. 'I know this is big stuff for you both to deal with.'

'Thank you. No. Yes. I mean, it is.'

Dr Carr introduced us to my ward doctor, who will oversee my chemotherapy 'infusions'. His name is Karl. He showed us the rooms where I will sit when they wire me up each Wednesday. A long line of men and women sat propped up with pillows and cushions, attached intravenously to drips, reading and doing crosswords and looking for all the world like they were at the hairdressers. I did ask her about the hair, as it was something I knew Shimi would ask later. She blinked again. 'Yes, you will lose your hair. And there may be other side effects too, but we won't worry about those for now.'

Karl is tall, skinny and almost shaven-headed. 'It's no secret,' Dr Carr whispered two seconds before introducing him, 'that Karl has had chemotherapy himself. For Hodgkin's. He knows what you'll be going through.'

'So you're Anthony?' he grinned. 'And you must be Mrs Anthony.'

He turned to me again. 'Don't expect politeness here,' he smiled, nodding backwards at the room.

'I'll bring my Chelsea scarf then.'

'You and I are *not* going to get on,' and he gave me a half-hug, his arm reaching round me, pulling my shoulder into him.

'Fantastic,' I said. 'I wouldn't want you being nice.'

Dr Carr had finished by saying 'Not the nicest news on Valentine's Day. Take each other out for a nice lunch, if you can.'

'I have to get back to work,' Tatty said.

Which we had predicted, so had had a romantic lunch at Dart's Farm the day before, steak (her) and Mediterranean chicken (me) with – shock – wine. Delicious. A mosey round the shop for bread and chocolate, then home.

We sat watching the curling at the Olympics. The commentator referred to the 'ever-increasing tension' of the game, while his partner, not to be outdone, claimed 'the curling has been pretty aggressive this afternoon, unbelievable in fact.' Tatty looked at the screen and said 'It's a housewives game! They've all got highlights, they stand around gossiping, then get to work with dusters and brushes.'

Unlike many of our friends and family we have restricted ourselves to looking at a single website, lymphoma dot org, the official site of the Lymphoma Association.

You download a PDF file which tells you all the variants of the disease, their symptoms, treatments and side effects. I had no idea lymphoma was such a large family. I lost count of the different varieties, hungry only for information about what the hell was happening to me.

I learned three things. The first, which Dr Carr had also told me, is that no one knows how you get NHL, or where it comes from. Second, the kind of NHL I have, diffuse large B-cell lymphoma (DLBCL) is the most common kind, with about 3,000 new cases per year. Lastly, NHL is a cancer of the white blood cells. In my case, it is the white blood cells which produce the antibodies which fight off infection. Both literally and metaphorically, my body has attacked itself. No wonder people reach so easily for the description of cancer as a 'battle' which the patient must 'fight'.

I toyed with finding out the difference between large B-cell lymphoma and large T-cell lymphoma but gave up, my E at O level biology coming back to taunt me. All I need to know, really, is that I'm very ill and that the treatment to make me better is going to make me feel even worse.

Later we watched *Bruce Almighty* outtakes with Bendy, who is off-school. There's a deleted scene where Bruce is being shown by God the outcomes of his having said 'yes' to the world's prayers. One lady, on being told she was bankrupt, slipped on some milk in a supermarket, sued and bought a condo in Florida. But God said that if he'd answered the prayer properly she'd have had to swallow her pride and talk to her sister and learn some humility. A boy routinely being bullied at school had his prayer answered and became a wrestling champion then a steroids addict instead of the outstanding poet of his generation. 'The bullying was his material and you took it away from him. Sometimes,' he went on, 'to make a good picture you've got to use some dark colours.'

16 February

On Merenna's last night with us before her trip – the night *of* the trip: I had to drop her off at the school at half-eleven – I made everyone's favourite, lemon chicken with pesto, rice and peas. They destroyed the lot. Shim said 'It's the only good chicken recipe you do. The rest is rubber.'

While making it I played *A Walk Across The Rooftops*, and was astonished to find that it is still the Great Album I thought it was when I sat up half the night convincing anyone who'd listen as a student.

There's a lovely bit in Giles Smith's *Lost in Music* (the Cocteau Twins chapter, as it happens) when he describes the album as 'painstakingly miserable', the music 'scrupulously pared away to the noise of someone tapping despairingly on a radiator'. And then this: 'it's an astonishing record, especially if you've got cancer.'

I'd forgotten that part of his story. The bit about the radiator is true, though, even if he is wrong about it being miserable. Like me, he finds he can still listen to them: 'they proved too good, too resilient to be used and disposed of.' Listening to it again, I know why: there's hardly anything there. The key phrase of Smith's is not the radiator being tapped, but the 'pared away.' Their gift, it seems to me, is chiefly one of suggestion. The music feels full, but is essentially spare. This is true of their lyrics too, which I see now more as an extended free verse poem which somehow has been made to sound like a narrative. It is beguilingly intimate, yet you never really find out what on earth is going on.

When I recover from this disease I will celebrate by writing an essay with the title: 'Minimalist Urban Odysseys: The Blue Nile's Debt to William Carlos Williams's Red Wheelbarrow.'

Why did it take me so long to buy it on CD? I find it works just as well as it ever did, though I am embarrassed to say I can remember exactly the kind of thing I used to write about it (who was I writing for?), with phrases like 'crystalline brilliance', 'superbly crafted' and 'heart-rending'. As a soundtrack to falling in and out of love, it was perfect. As a life-affirming soundtrack to coming to terms with cancer – or just cooking chicken – it is the real thing.

'What's it like, telling people?' said Rich on the phone, again.

'It's like watching a film in which you are also the main character. You're not pleased with your performance.'

I felt this especially yesterday, when I went in to work to tell my students, moving from room to room. Pin-drop silences, and lots of very wide eyes. I slipped in the gag that with my youth and fitness – and good looks, ha ha – the prognosis is 80%+; and that anyway it's not like I have much hair to lose. One girl I found outside afterwards in tears being comforted by a friend. 'It's just that my mother's cancer's just come back. It's in her liver and lungs and bones,' she said. It wasn't easy.

I said to Rich, 'The other kind of lymphoma, the low-grade sort, just sits around all day watching Channel 4 Racing. Much harder to deal with. My sort wants to go to Ibiza and sleep around. They can tackle that one head-on.'

Later I was on the phone-marathon. Nic called my email 'beautifully crafted'; and Charlotte said they were like poems: 'Keep them, they're fantastic.' But nothing prepares you for the lack of preparedness in someone's eyes when you tell them face to face. 'Oh my God.' 'Fuck.' 'I'm so sorry.' 'Is there anything we can do?' My most frequent response to this is: 'Don't lose touch.'

17 February

The great thing (there are so many!) about having cancer is the retail therapy. I had my Christmas-money-copy of *Pink Moon* on when *Made to Love Magic* arrived. It's like having a rather talented but otherwise monosyllabic older brother busking in the drawing room. I played it the morning of going to see the consultant, suddenly spooked by Drake's barehanded admission of his need of others. 'Black Eyed Dog' didn't exactly improve things later on. I'm still glad to have it around, though. That Larkin thing about a good poem/song about despair being better than a bad one about happiness.

Last night we lay in bed reading the literature on the study I'm being invited on. Its title is 'A Multicentre randomised clinical trial comparing Rituximab and CHOP given every 14 days with Rituximab and CHOP given every 21 days for the treatment of patients with newly diagnosed diffuse large B-cell non-Hodgkin's lymphoma.' Pithy. Acronym: 'R-CHOP 14 vs. 21'. Basically they want to know if the life chances are better if they nuke you every two weeks, compared to the more standard three.

Even if I'm in the trial, I still may get it every three weeks, as they have to have a control group. And it's a computer that picks me, just like on Goal of the Month.

It's a chilling list of side effects:

sore mouth
diarrhoea (mild)
nausea and vomiting
low blood count (increased risk of bleeding and infection)
loss of head and body hair
numbness or tingling sensation in hands and feet only

Well, not so chilling actually. But that's just the CHOP effects. Rituximab takes it to a whole new level:

fever
chills
headache
achy muscles and joints
itching
redness of skin
nausea and mild drop in blood pressure

Most of these go after the first treatment – phew – or start to decrease. They were at pains to tell me if the side effects are really bad, then they have drugs for those too. I pick up my first patch of anti-uric-acid tablets today.

The thing which scares me most is knowing that to get better I am going to have to feel shit for a while: a long tunnel approaching, the sides of which your headlights don't fully illuminate.

18 February

Sitting propped up in bed while Tatty plays with her new mobile. There's a lot to be grateful for. Wes and Allie and baby Olivia passed through last night with fizz and hugs and banter. And finally a good phone call, Gill, the Research Nurse at Haematology, saying yes I have been accepted onto the trial and it will be every two weeks instead of every three, making the treatment more intense, but shorter. We got the diary out last night and I put luminous green C's and R's on the days of treatment and recovery, two weeks apart. If all goes well the chemotherapy (CHOP) finishes on 2nd May and the Rituximab on 30 May.

On the way back from hospital from our meeting with Gill we passed an old-school electricity station on a side alley, with yellow warning signs of flashing lightning. Next to it, in plain black felt tip, another sign in clear handwriting: 'The Door to the Other Life.'
'Weird,' said Tatty.
'How did they know?' I said.

Gill said the hair might come back curly and a different colour.
'As long as it isn't red,' I said.
'You never know,' she deadpanned.

Tatty describes the Haematology unit as like being in the business class waiting room at an airport. It's very hushed, with curvy walls of different colours, a yellow one meeting a blue, and the chairs are a kind of mottled pink which probably goes under the name of 'frosted heather'. The magazines are better quality, too: no Heat or Angler's Monthly; it's all Country Living and SAGA. I was reading the latter as we were called in for our first chat with Felicity. It was an interview with Ned Sherrin, who said the three essentials of life were food, drink, and taxis. The best thing about growing old, he said, was 'slaying the beast of sexual desire'.

There's a café in the waiting room. You get a real china mug and carrot cake 'homemade by our volunteers'. There is a lot of touching of arms and laughter. The nurse who saw me yesterday made small-talk with a grey haired lady (a former patient in for a check-up, I'd guess) for fully five minutes, two yards away from where we sat, never once losing interest or eye contact. Karl, exuding positivity and cheeriness, bounded in at one point and made a joke about her not needing makeup because she looked so young.

Gill let us ask questions (mostly Tatty, as I had gone a bit blank), then talked through the implications of the trial. I can pull out at any time; and it all remains completely confidential. The main things to clear up were that I *won't* be spending Wednesday night in the ward; and that I am allowed to continue to drink.

'Of course, you may find after a while you don't want to. Some people just lose their taste for it.'

'OK.'

'Or their taste altogether,' she said.

They will want me to drink 2–3 litres of water a day, to flush out the drugs once it has started work on the tumour. And my fruit consumption will have to go up, to avoid constipation. If I go two days 'without going' I am to call them. Ditto if my temperature goes over 38 °C, day or night. There's a long list of numbers I am going to become extremely familiar with. The main givens are hair loss and lethargy. 'It's very possible you will be knocked out a bit,' she said.

Later Robyn and Rory are coming round to drink with us and eat beef casserole (in that order). Robyn saw Tats in the street today and said plainly 'Prepare him to feel rubbish, I did.' Even though the length of treatment is shorter than six months, it does frighten the shit out of me, the idea of entering the tunnel voluntarily, with barely a speck of light at the end of it.

Tatty has been reading the leaflet on NHL to me. It says by

2025 lymphoma will be as common as breast, lung, skin and colon cancer. It is increasing in Europe more than the 'developing world' and in the UK grows by 4% a year.

I said: 'For the first time in my life I'm ahead of the crowd.'

19 February

A good evening last night with Robyn and Rory and Paul and Sally. Lots of banter, laughter, and alcohol. Bruschetta in the sitting room with fizz and olives, Bourguignon with mash, then Sally's brownies and cream. They all caught the vibe brilliantly, with Paul brandishing his own bottle of pop as he came in. We talked, like all middle class parents, about schools; and as Rory and I always seem to at some level, about Monkton, but without bitterness. It was good having Robyn there. She was quite clear about the horrors awaiting me, without once being morbid: 'They are basically going to poison you and you're going to feel crap.'

We left the debris in the kitchen at half-midnight, then collapsed. I woke at 3, then 6, remaining awake for half an hour to an hour, before conking out till about 9. Feeling pretty shattered, increasingly so, esp. in the evenings. Someone said tonight that I must write it all down. 'It's a question of staying awake,' I replied, mindful of what Felicity Carr had said to me about how I would have begun to feel 'quite unwell' had they not found it when they did. I like the understatement here. Also, as in her 'pretty rough time' to describe the effects of chemo. She's been lovely, sparkly, and honest, her remarks like some sort of code you can only interpret by thinking of the worst thing she might be saying, then letting that be the subtext.

20 February

A shattering day.

Woke up, for the first time since being in hospital earlier in January, feeling achey, stiff, as if I hadn't slept at all. The pattern at the moment seems to be: drop off, then around 3, or 4, wake up for a bit, fall off again, wake up for the loo, then wake more fully between 5 and 6, dropping off again around 6.30, just as Tatty wakes up and the day begins. 'I'm awake if you want to talk,' she says into the darkness, waking me properly.

A rawness in the wind today, a day for hat *and* gloves, in spite of the feeble sun. Get used to this? I don't want to.

21 February

What does cancer do? It takes away your children's hobbies. Shimi had already had a row with Tats about going swimming with a cold, about how Daddy's white blood cells are going to come down and that I was going to need to stay healthy. Having had no success, he tried me, in the middle of trying to clear my desk of the last pressing work emails. I turned to him and said firmly that he would receive absolutely no sympathy, should his cough get worse. The same look of panic welled up in his eyes once again. Then I turned back to my emails, withdrawing eye contact completely, and he telephoned Sam to say when should they meet up at the pool.

Part of me really admires his obstinacy, I have to admit it.

This is not the worst moment so far. For that we thank church.

Two minutes before the service I was asked if they could pray for me. Out of politeness and surprise I said that would be fine. But I forgot to tell Tatty and the children. I do not think I can forgive myself the look of wild panic in Shimi's eyes when he realised it would happen and there was no turning back. Merenna said later the worst bit was the line about 'the family facing this terrible time'. 'They couldn't even be bothered to use our real names,' she said.

Vicky has arrived to look after us on my first chemo day

tomorrow. She bore flowers from Non, who apologises they are all white, which in Austria would be unforgivable, because white is for death.

'I would never have noticed,' I said.

A fragment from supper with the gang on Saturday: Robyn holding forth entertainingly about research into chemotherapy starting after the First World War, when they noticed that gassing troops in the trenches actually alleviated certain symptoms or illnesses some of them had. I had no idea of this little-known tale. 'They basically realised that poisoning people could have beneficial effects. That's where the drugs found in much chemotherapy first got used,' she said.

The other little-known fact of the evening, from her knowledge of National Trust properties, is that, because they are looked after so well, they use NT yew trees in many of the drugs that make up chemo-type cocktails. 'So you'll be poisoned by high-quality yew clippings from Devon,' she giggled.

Chemotherapy

22 February

First day of chemo.

We got to the hospital early and waited, looking at but not really seeing the magazines, including the ironically titled *Devon Life*.

In the way that the world divides into people who instinctively save or kill spiders, ignore or make tea for their builder, and support either the red or the blue team on the pitch, I now know of a less spoken of club: those who have had, or have not had, chemotherapy.

My image of it until today was that a doctor wired you up to a vat of chemicals, walked away and left you to it. It's much more intimate than that. And, being my first time, slower, too.

First there is the wait to check that the 'script' (hospital jargon for internal prescription) is both present and correct. Mine was neither. First Nadine, politely, and then Karl, with a flourish of Anglo-Saxon, phoned up the pharmacy. Karl winked at us with a grin while he swore at them. Putting the phone down he said 'The trouble with the NHS is that all the wankers in it work in pharmacy. Right then, Anthony. I think you're ready to start being poisoned.'

Everyone in the room laughed.

He gets away with it because he has been through it himself.

In the shorter wait that remained, Nadine clothed herself in her 'blues', protective clothing worn over the ones she had on already, including gloves, headgear like a shower-cap, and a mask.

'What are those for?' I asked.

She hesitated for a second. 'Well, as you know, you know, it's pretty poisonous stuff we're giving you. We wouldn't want it going anywhere. If we spilled any we'd have to close the whole ward down. It would take a whole day to clean up.'

'They're that nasty are they?'

'They are indeed.'

And the subject was closed.

I was ushered into a large green reclining armchair. A pillow was placed under my arm and my blood taken. Nadine poured onto the table next to me twenty tiny cherry red capsules and a beaker of milk to wash them down with.

'Milk?' I said.

'They're your steroids. You're supposed to take them with food, but we find a glass of milk's just as good. You take twenty of these each day for the next five days, first thing in the morning.'

'At breakfast?'

'That's right, steroids for breakfast.'

As I began swallowing them down a large package arrived, wrapped in voluminous amounts of protective plastic packaging. Nadine swivelled to Karl and read him the label out loud. After each line she paused, while he also read it, then he too read each item, my name, address, date of birth and hospital number out loud, followed by the litany of the drugs they were about to inject into me: Cylcophosphamide, Hydroxy-daunorubicin and Oncovin.

Next Nadine tipped out two Paracetamol, handing me a beaker of water.

'What's this for?' I said. 'I haven't got a headache.'

'Oh, we find it helps people when we start the injections. It takes the pain away.'

'Pain?'

'Pain, yes. In your arms.'

'Right.'

She began attaching the first needle.

'But before anything else, we give you one of these as well, to take the edge of it all.'

'What is it?'

'Piriton.'

'The antihistamine? Like for hay fever?'

'Like for hay fever, yes.'

'What's it do?'

'Sends you away with the fairies, basically.'

I looked at her.

'This isn't going to be fun, is it?'

To her credit, she held my eye without flinching. 'No, my dear, it isn't.'

24 February

Yesterday was raw, sleet in the air, trees black with wet against the grey sky. Rawness everywhere. Today it is trying to snow and Shimi has been for a toboggan on the moor with Sam.

We spent the day being just the two of us, mooching at home, lunch in town, shopping, then back for supper and a vid. Merenna and Shimi out the whole day, with Vix, being treated. Found I had energy, so used it.

Went to Zizzi's, for a very good pizza, an asparagus special with mozzarella etc. for Tats. Nattered about my family, who seem to want hourly updates and are more than keen to come down at every opportunity. Slight tension in the air at the house today because of it, not because Tatty and I disagree, but because we do agree and it's really my call to make and I don't want to upset them.

What they won't know until we tell them is that Tatty is an inch away from being signed off with stress; that the phone does not stop ringing; that Merenna is viral/post-viral and is not better yet, despite having had two weeks off; and that we just want to go on being normal. I certainly don't want them coming down the day of the treatment and watch me being injected. For one thing, it'll be painful for them, another, boring. If I suddenly get ill, then yes, please, come, otherwise can you just come for the day and possibly break the journey with Rich in Bath? It sounds awful even thinking it, let alone writing it down. But it is the truth, and we have to tell it.

Am being a good boy, eating my fruit and drinking my

water and not worrying about my calories, as Nadine said. Lunch today from Nat Thomas (10 points for no dishes to return): tortilla wraps with grated cheese, refried beans, guacamole and sour cream. 'The best we've had so far', pronounced Tats.

Lots of funny phone calls. Janet in tears to Tats, giving advice about how to deal with relatives after her own sister died so quickly, then saying let's go for a drink. A collector's item from Hannah, on ansaphone, 'trying to be chipper' and sounding like death, not surprisingly as she has flu. I wish if they felt crap they would rather not assume I'd like to share in it. A good one from James Bradley, who always uses the right biological words and gives me answers for names and drugs before I've dragged them from memory. Don't think he was ready for me to confess how much my wee smells, but he seemed to have an explanation: 'That'll be your kidneys and liver excreting your [scientific term] so that your body doesn't [scientific verb] an [scientific noun].' 'Right. Thanks.'

Becca Alexander popped in 'on a double yellow' as we were finishing lunch. She's been to see her reflexologist, who has lent me a plastic wallet of alternative guff about Native American Indian methods of treating cancer etc., all of it badly photocopied. It came with a photograph-card of the NT gardens at Heligan, with an instruction 'to return them to me as soon as you have finished with them as I don't have any other copies.' That'll be today, then.

People do what they do. Reacting and acting, I think, as much for themselves as they do for you. The poets are all amazing, 'putting out healing vibes into the universe', some of them even promising prayers. The neighbours all offer 'anything they can do'.

Two lovely letters, one from an old school friend acknowledging the uselessness of offering 'anything we can do' from Jersey; and the other from Amy, offering to sit and be with me and drink coffee, give a lift, whatever. A letter of presence and absence. As James Bradley put it 'I'm a space person. Or as I sometimes say, a sociable introvert.' The rarest of people seem to have pulled this trick off so far.

Today at the doctors with Bendy waiting for her appointment with the nurse, a memory of our old neighbour Cyril in Brixton. His take on Beckett's *Endgame*, having watched an actor-neighbour playing the part of Clov, was that it was like watching a play in an old people's home, with all its references to painkillers.

An old lady staggered in today who was pure Beckett. She began talking randomly to the woman opposite her.

'Was I here yesterday?'

'Yes you were.'

'Was I? Here? Yesterday?'

'Yes.'

'I think I was here yesterday. At least I think I was. I said to him I'll never move like this again. And that was ten years ago.'

'You were here yesterday.'

'Thought I was. I told him.'

Saturday 25 February

A day of gifts.

We began with tears as I couldn't face doing my injections, even into my leg. 'Nurse Tatty' took over, as if she'd been doing them all her life. She filled up the little vials, carefully squeezing the air bubble so it wouldn't start squirting, matter-of-factly saying 'These are the ones that save your life.' It's called GCSF (or Lengorastin), for the build-up of white blood cells. Amazing to think there's a French cyclist somewhere right at this moment doing the same thing to build up his red ones, then an injection to take away the traces so he won't be caught cheating.

A lovely letter, the first in years, from Dale in Harringey, who has taken up fishing again and has a slug-infested allotment. He sounds on energetic and generous form, warm-spirited and open, as I remember him ('but then I've always had a good life.') He's got high cholesterol so's had to give up dairy, which I can't believe, as I still see him chomping through the cheese counter, methodically trying out different varieties of cheddar as a student, and layering every piece of toast with double-butter.

His mum has died (of cancer) since we've spoken. He says the end was good, in spite of the rubbish prognosis, that he got to nurse her 'with real nurses' for the final months. I'm sad to hear she's gone. She was the one I nervously rang up to ask where he was living so I could ring him five years ago. I think she even bought my book.

And a friend of his, having recovered from chemo, says he now has more energy than for years. 'Who knows' he says, without adding a question mark.

A lovely card from Dana, too, complete with '4 chemotherapy treatments.' 1 is a landscape, 2 is a poem, 3 is a prayer and 4 is laughter, a collection of George Bush's *bon mots* regarding literacy education. The poem is one I don't know, by Brian Patten, called 'After Frost':

> It's hard to tell what bird it is
> Singing in the misty wood,
> Or the reason for its song
> So late after evening's come.
>
> When all else dropped its name
> Down into the scented dark,
> Its song grown cool and clear says
> Nothing much to anyone.
>
> But catches hold a whisper in my brain
> that only now is understood.
> It says, rest your life against this song,
> It's rest enough for anyone.

I sat reading it at the breakfast table in a kind of hopeful silence, the one I always bring to a poem I don't know, in expectation that it will do something. I didn't have long to wait to feel the hairs on my arms prickle or my eyes to start stinging. The thing is, I apprehended it at first purely musically by its sense, not really aware of the meaning at all. But I found it so moving, aware that here were some very simple words laid out in a straightforward way in such a combination as to lift you out of everything for a minute, while putting you more at the centre of that thing than anything before. It's the mystery I constantly chase and crave, as reader and writer.

The prayer is good too, by Carmina Gadelica (III):

> God to enfold me,
>   God to surround me,
> God in my speaking,
>   God in my thinking.
>
> God in my sleeping,
>   God in my waking,
> God in my watching,
>   God in my hoping.

Again, completely simple, but devastating.

Then the George Bush-isms: 'You teach a child to read, and he or she will be able to pass a literacy test' (February 21, 2001). Hilarious. Chilling. And then this:

> I want it to be said that the Bush administration was a results-orientated administration, because I believe the results and focusing our attention and energy on teaching children to read and having an education system that's responsive to the child and to the parents, as opposed to mired in a system that refuses to change, will make America what we want it to be – a more literate country and a hopefuller country.

Sunday 26 February

6 am

Bizarre to say it, but find I can be up at six writing, making tea and eating bread and jam creeping round the house like the old days waiting for the heating to come on.

Not a good night. Woke with night sweats once and had to pee at least twice. Knew it was useless around 4.25, but stayed in bed hoping sleep might come, turning slowly not to wake Tatty. Finally threw in the towel at 5.45.

The night sweats do scare me as they are – fatigue aside, plus the pain of the tumour on the urethra, which isn't the same thing as the tumour itself hurting – the only symptoms I clearly have. Somewhere on an envelope there is a scrawl I made at four-something about three weeks ago. I was wide awake but desperate to get back to bed, aching and shivering. I don't know if there's mileage there. Probably not. But what made me do it was the fear, plus the certainty, of losing those lines if I didn't get them down. I may have all tomorrow night to work on them, if I want.

27 February

Another great thing about having cancer is that you look in the mirror and there's Brian Eno staring back at you.

We performed the hair-ceremony with the honorary slap-heads in my life – Claude and Nicky Fagan – bringing the tools of their trade. In Claude's case a simple set of professional clippers; in Nicky's razors, creams and oils, which I am not ready for.

In the end it was Shim who did the job. Fearless, he plugged in the clippers and began shaving my head, expertly shielding my eyes from falling hair with his hand across my forehead, and changing angle of attack like a natural. Tatty took photos on her mobile (Charlotte says I look like De Niro in *Taxi Driver* in one of them) and the boys and Bendy looked on, bantering and eating Claude's biscuits. Bendy finished the whole thing by placing a sample of hair inside an envelope with the inscription

R.I.P
hair of Anthony
Charles Wilson
26.2.06

which sounds a little previous but it is just her way of dealing with it: 'so mum can keep some of it.'

A joyous calm day. We began at Maya and Tim's for pancakes and coffee and chat around the table. Expertly and sensitively they helped us talk about IT as much as we wanted, Maya making sure that she got a good sesh with each of us moving round the chairs. The whole thing loving and warm. Abs drew me a get well card wearing Tim's Panama hat, which he had had me model earlier as we talked about retail therapy on the net.

Robyn popped her head round the door later. After a couple of minutes of chat I realised we were talking to each other not as neighbours but as members of Chemotherapy Anonymous, swapping stories and impressions of the process as though it was what we always talked about in the hallway on Sunday night while she waited for Sam to come down.

'You know that itchy bottom feeling when they first inject you? That'll get worse,' she said. 'It ends up like you're sitting on a hairbrush.'

'I'll look forward to it.'

'And the waking up at 4.31, that's the steroids making you hyper, that's normal too.'

'And the night sweats?'

'Oh I still get those.'

'Oh.'

'You just have to try not to eat too much, though that's what you feel like the whole time.'

'Absolutely.'

'Not that you'll have any problem getting rid of it of course, not like me.'

'I wouldn't say that.'

'It took me ages to feel normal again.'

Tuesday 28 February

Sitting in the kitchen. A beautiful day, raw again but bright, bright, little fluffy clouds scudding in the blue.

Walked Shim to school and felt – for the first time – really whacked having done nothing at all. Feel weedy and a bit sorry for myself. 'Which you are allowed,' as Tatty keeps reminding me, but still feels like giving in somehow.

Yesterday another of gifts as Sarah came to visit. We sat in the kitchen while the window cleaner worked his way through the house, drinking coffee and talking. Suddenly it was lunchtime. She took me out to the café at the end of the road. When we got back she said, 'You lie down for a bit, I'll just sit and read.' She timed it perfectly, knowing I think before I did that I suddenly felt knocked out and wouldn't be up to much that afternoon. She made Bendy some toast and juice, and Shim some tea when he came in.

She looks well. She's still moving stiffly on her knee, especially up and down stairs. I noticed as we sat going over the story in the kitchen how alive her face is, open in an alert way, but not at all childish. She is very good company and easy to talk to. No pressure to be profound or make a big statement. A huge gift.

Going over the story made me realise just how quick the whole thing has been, less than a calendar month from ultrasound to the start of treatment. Looking back, today, in my weariness, I can see how I have taken it all so well, calmly, cheerily, easing people into conversation about it for fear of their reactions. Today I feel very different. Not just knocked out, but in pain a little too, from the tumour-pressure, plus the general weirdness that goes on all the time inside the insides, that feeling of 'am I about to throw up, or is it just ravenous hunger again?' Today, with that, for the first time, fear. The nagging question of what if it doesn't work despite the prognosis? The fear of death, or, more specifically, of being conquered by something. Chris Richards says I have to be determined, to fight it off, but I've read things which say this makes no difference. He is onto something, possibly, but for the first time, just in these quiet sunny kitchen minutes, I feel like a lot of fight has gone out of me.

Walking back from dropping off Shim today I saw Laura stuck in traffic in her Volvo. I pulled off my hat to show her, knowing she hadn't seen me bald. The gasp and falling forward onto her steering wheel in surprise were worth it.

A sudden feeling, just before this, of being public property. A young mum who I always pass going in the opposite direction, and who I have spoken to properly once, half-paused to wish me 'good luck with your treatment'. You don't have control over who knows, I know that, and I don't really care. I just wasn't prepared to feel so unexpectedly touched, mixed in with an ounce of cross-ness at being 'discussed', which in turn became guilt.

Wednesday 1 March

Incredible rinsed light today, very transparent. A dull breeze after yesterday's snow showers, with promise of more, but so far none. Intense blue and pressure climbing as it says in that Ted Hughes poem . . .

Not pleased with my performance yesterday, too liberal a use of the word 'feel'. You are going to feel shit. Get used to it. 4/10. See me.

The most likely thing is that it's not having those lovely steroids to take. Hence being able to sleep. Hence zero energy? While I was sleeping, did Daffy Duck get his cricket bat and whack me in the face with it? Pace yourself.

Spent the day avoiding picking up the phone, except to Chris to turn his visit down. Sim and Is have been promising a visit. I had the proverbial 'on a train' call from Is at tea time. At least I was up by then.

Today I kicked off (as usual) with *Will and Grace* then *Frasier*, both of which seem faultless, in their way. Complete worlds, little clockwork universes sealed off from reality.

Amazing what cancer makes you crave. US sitcoms. Broccoli. Marmite. And, from nowhere, three slices of peanut buttered bread. But broccoli especially. Tatty said, watching Merenna hiding hers, 'She's not your daughter is she?' I buy them Danish pastries for after school, like I always have, determined to Keep Things Normal.

Bumped into Maya walking back from School this morning and she nearly attacked me when I whipped my hat off. 'Anthony, it's *gorgeous*. Really *gorgeous*. You look great! You should keep it like that!' Buying bread after my sleep I showed it off to Dawn. 'Really suits you, you know. What a lovely shaped head!'

Another great spin-off of cancer: non-threatening conversations with women in which they tell you how attractive you are.

Before I conk out again . . . we watched the Poliakoff play on Sunday night (*Gideon's Daughter*). I've always had a soft spot for him. *Perfect Strangers* I thought *was* perfect, the slow unfolding more like a symphony than a play. And when I read at Ways With Words with Peter two years ago, it was the queue to see him snaking round the lawn which we competed with. No contest.

Bill Nighy 'played himself' according to the *Guardian* review, which is right, I think. Not as self–consciously as in *Love Actually* or *Hitchiker's Guide,* but the ticks were all present: unnecessary pauses between words, as if to draw attention to significance which wasn't there; the lurching forward a whole inch towards someone and then stopping dead, hesitating, pausing, going 'Er . . .'

I loved it, though. I think P is more of a poet than a dramatist, in that not actually very much happens but that it looks gorgeous and continually sends shivers down your spine while finding its way towards saying something. He makes *great* images. The choir in the church. The party in the Indian restaurant.

The key scene led to explain why Nighy's daughter had drifted away from him. His wife (to whom he has been unfaithful) is dying of cancer in hospital. A complete stranger walks into their room, sits down next to them and starts talking. After seeing him out he goes to make a phone call. By the time he comes back, half an hour later, she has died and the talking man is back: 'the nurses thought he was touchy.' The daughter cannot forgive that he wasn't there at the end. I love the mixture in this of the everyday, the tragic and the odd; randomness ramming itself up against our own small griefs. It works because it works because it works.

On the way back from school with Shim, he told me his day in detail for the first time ever. 'We took a vote on games, double English or double Maths. Double English won 'cos Mr Willey said it was too icy.'

'Which did you vote?'

'Double English.'

'Was that good?'

'Yeh it was 'cos we're doing adverts – we have to look at an advert then say what it makes us feel.'

'And what did you do?'

'There was that one for Cancer Research, you know, where she says my mother shouldn't be here, so at the end I said it made me reassured. To fill up the page.'

He looked at me, smiling, wanting me to smile my approval.

'I feel reassured anyway,' he stated. 'But it was a good thing to say because it made the writing a bit longer.'

2 March

Three days of zonked-outness, today a weird shivering ache, on a pulse, every twenty seconds, down my right side. I've just had a cheese sandwich and tried watching *ER* but it was too much. The *ER* I mean. It began, cheerily, with a pregnant woman waking in a freezing flat, her waters broken, to find that both her children and her husband were all unconscious with carbon monoxide poisoning. It sent me over the edge. I stumbled back in here, under my rug.

I finished a book today. Donald Miller's *Blue Like Jazz*, a book of short essays, apercus, really, on the theme of finding God. It has a lot going for it over other Christian books (not that I'm an expert) in that it is a) well written and b) relentlessly honest. I like his narrative voice a lot, with references to Andrew the Protestor and Tony the Beat Poet (who isn't one at all). He reminds me of my favourite voices, Billy Collins, Anne Lamott, Carol Shields or Frank O'Hara at Fire Island. They're scatty, a little frayed at the edges, a little bit basically screwy, like me. I like that. Miller has it in spades.

There's a really good passage near the end of the book about cancer. In a preamble which goes on to explain how most Christian language about love (*valuing* people, *investing* in them) is in the metaphor of economics, he exposes the truth behind most discourse about cancer. It is written, or spoken, in the metaphor of war. He calls for a different way of looking at the disease, which does not put the responsibility for recovery onto the patient, who in most cases is already frightened and exhausted enough without this extra burden.

As Billy Collins puts it in 'Marginalia' this had me standing and cheering in the bleachers.

Later

I finally feel like I have cancer.

I have just called the hospital re my aching back and waves of stiffening pain. 'What are you being treated for?' they said. 'Large B-cell diffuse non-Hodgkin's lymphoma.'

I felt a bit smug, it came off so pat.

'Are you on Lengorastin for your white blood count?'

'Yes, since Saturday.'

'It's probably that, then. It is a common side effect, I'm afraid.'

I asked if I could take Paracetamol for it and she said yes I could. 'Let us know how you get on,' she said.

I think what you want is a list which takes you through what you'll feel. Something along the lines of:

> The first day of treatment you are going to throw up in the evening because let's face it you are full of poison and you will lie down too quickly, not having been told that to do so brings on the nausea very forcefully and that staying upright is your best bet.
>
> The next morning you are going to feel sick again, but won't be. Instead you will notice how something like a nuclear reaction seems to be going off below your diaphragm. You will carry your sick bucket around the house with you, sit near the loo for long periods, and walk close to hedges when you leave the house. You will pee almost constantly. If you remember to drink fluids as we encouraged you it will run clear. If you forget, your pee will look like *Pinot Noir* and stink like a sewer. This is normal.
>
> You will lie awake at night and 'wake up' fully at hours previously known to you through baby-care. You will notice the dark and the cold, your thoughts clanking in your head as they pace through your skull. You will get up 'for one more pee' only to throw the towel in at 5.02 sitting in

the kitchen leafing through old copies of *The Express and Echo*, convinced that you recognise the photograph of the child on page 3.

You will take twenty minutes to down all your drugs. It is not the swallowing you find hard, just the sheer quantity. You like them best with chocolate milk. Then a banana. Then some dried apricots. Then some toast. Then some marmite, on the knife. You notice you have not been making any bowel movements. You eat more dried apricots, more toast. You 'leave it a day'. And find you go twice, either side of lunch, which is baked beans on toast plus extra toast with bread and butter while you wait for them to cook. You find you have 'limitless' energy, the kind which sends you into town to the library and considering buying coffee. You smile a lot, especially at the school gate. The nuclear reaction seems to be dying down a bit. You go out for pizza. It is really not so bad, were it not for the headaches. You try a tiny sip of wine over supper. You wake with an axe through your head. This goes on all week. Except you skip the wine. You call the hospital. They tell you this is normal.

Just when you are 'used to things' it hits you like a wave or sudden gust from behind a street corner. Fatigue is in everything you do. You lift your head from the pillow and it hurts. You notice your slippers make little scraping noises as you shuffle from room to room. You stay in one room, near the telly; you give thanks for the remote control. The phone rings but you do not answer it, even though it is six inches across the bed from you. You start to sleep for hours, waking from dreams about playing team sports as a teenager. But you crave sleep. You think you look good curled up.

And then the shivers start. Somewhere in your back above your kidneys a tense pulse that begins warmly and ends in a shudder near your spine throws long electrical currents. You think of an octopus, a giant squid. You think of *Dr Who*. You think of *Fawlty Towers*, what you would give to be watching it for the first time, with your father, scarcely able to believe your luck, your luminous happiness. And then it goes. It comes back when you cook the children pasta. It is one of your best sauces ever and you are bent double. You notice you have run out of pepper. You think about ringing the hospital. While the children eat, they joke and eye you, warily. You tell them it is nothing. You go back to feeling merely exhausted. It has snowed outside. The government have won a vote. England are back in the Test. You know you will survive.

Sunday 5 March

Morning

Propped up in bed listening to Tatty reading *Old Yeller* to Shim, one of her favourite childhood books. Amazon really is a great thing. Waterstone's just go 'Uh?' at you. She does a great Southern drawl, very expressive, *Gone with the Wind* vs. *Steel Magnolias*, her favourite films.

Saturday I had energy, until about one minute after lunch, and the day was dazzling. We walked into town with the boy, changed CDs at the library and ate paninis at BTP. I have a really heavy cold and spend most of the night coughing. At BTP a Tats-type panic over my keys, suddenly missing. They were at the library all along and I thanked them for saving my life, which is still the kind of thing I am allowed to say, even without thinking.

Bumped into Vince and Fiona in town. Vince said 'You looked a bit gaunt this week, I thought. I nearly ran you over to finish the job off.' Is it just me or is doctor-banter different class?

Sim and Is came by on Friday, stayed about an hour, then left. We sat a few minutes in the sitting room before stepping up to the café for 'the best lasagne I have ever tasted.' It's lovely being with them, their warm companionable universe where nothing is really harmful, or too much trouble.

Sim told a great story, which could very well be made up, 'from my days in telly', when he got to sit in on the over-dubbing into Arabic of the Eric Sykes film *The Plank*. The plot ('It either makes you laugh or it doesn't,' interrupted Is. 'It doesn't for me.') apparently involves Eric Sykes walking through a village with a plank on his shoulder. Hilarity ensues every time he turns to talk to someone. Many windows are smashed also. 'We laughed so much in the booth, my friend and I, we got chucked out. This was in Beirut, you know. It's all digital now.' 'But doesn't someone going 'aah!' when they've been hit by the plank sound more or less the same in Arabic?'

'No. In Arabic it's more of an 'urgh!' To his credit he said this with the straightest of faces.

Monday 6 March

Sitting up on the bed admiring the sunlight and feeling slightly headachy after my mid-morning coffee.

A poor night, waking at 3. I crept into the telly room and watched French football (PSG vs. Marseille). I did more or less the same on Saturday night, which was a toss up between boxing, *Conan the Barbarian*, weak comedy on Channel 4 and a John Mills Black-and-White where every accent was Mr Chulmley-Warner. I flicked between a dour lower-billed fight and the weak comedy, whose point was to make fun of rap music. A bit of an open goal, that, but you have to remember, it's post-pub, raging-munchies telly, so showing 50 Cent videos and asking archly 'Does rapping make you attractive?' is probably all you need to do to be thought of as incisively hilarious.

I switched to a documentary about volunteering at Glastonbury. They followed four young people, all doing their bit for, variously, Greenpeace (running a Free Love i.e. Blind

Date service), Water Aid ('Flushing out Poverty'), Oxfam and the hospital tent ('After the festival Jamie also signed up to do Reading'). They all looked sunburnt and very attractive. The Oxfam-guy was a steward on Gate 7, about a mile from the main action. One of his jobs was to bring tea out to his colleagues on the perimeter fence, then relieve them, at dawn. The camera expertly sat back as they swapped stories of people trying to get in brandishing knives. 'I was like woah, man!' He held his hands up, palms out, in front of him. 'You know, like, we don't need that kind of trouble.' 'Did they get nicked?' 'Yeh, the police piled in and got him,' he shrugged.

Next up was another volunteer-fest, telling two very different stories of confident Caroline and camera-shy Carl. Caroline (have a guess) was blonde, wore skimpy clothes and (guess what) got to massage people (really) in an occupational therapy ward in the gloomy European backwater of Barcelona. Cue lots of shots of her cooking in her flat and clapping along to her housemates' guitar playing. Carl 'had a number of issues at home' so got to work on a Norwegian commune with disabled people. 'They get you doing all sorts,' he sniffed. 'Cooking, cleaning, you know. But it's the wood chopping I'm best at. I build, you know. By the end of the day I've built a stack of wood and that makes me feel I've accomplished something. It's a good feeling.'

I couldn't decide who this was aimed at. Conscience-wracked student insomniacs who haven't sorted their summer holiday plans? Over on Channel 4 at the same time was more munchies-telly, of the baggy snowboarding variety. It consists of watching a succession of 18-year-old Norwegian and Canadian men competing to outdo each other on their 'two-seventy turns with grip' on approaching what look like three-quarter-inch stair-rails poking above the snow while the commentator shouts over a heavy metal soundtrack. Everything is 'amazing', 'spellbinding', 'hugely risky' and 'nerveless'. It cannot be sport, because only three people watching must know what is going on. If I were 19, however, and 'studying' for a

Sports Science degree five miles away from the nearest bus stop, I know which of the two programmes I'd be watching as I passed round the nachos.

Later

I watched *Planet Earth*, the Beeb's latest big budget nature programme, with Shim last night. An advert for public service broadcasting from start to finish, it was all the clichés and more: sumptuous, painstaking, breathtaking. One sequence showed the 'Amur' leopard from Russia (I thought it looked a bit like Speyside) of which there are about 40 left. David Attenborough deadpanned: 'A combination of irreversible climate change and inability to adapt to its new situation has pushed this extraordinary animal to the edge of extinction.' The footage of it – the first ever made – lasted about a minute. Television enacting the metaphor of its own message is what we grew up hoping it would be. Somehow this felt graver, sadder, more urgent, an elegy not just for rare mammals, but a whole approach to and vision of the medium itself.

Shim tucked himself into me – we both went wow at the slowed down footage of the Great White leaping to attack a seal – and kept lifting his head up to look at my eyes, to check if I was crying. I didn't, but he obviously sees more than I give him credit for.

He told me about his advert writing from last week on the way back from school today. 'You know that advert writing, where I said I was encouraged by Cancer Research, well it worked, I got two stickers, one at the top one at the bottom. I think she felt sorry for me.'

He's talking about school these days more than he ever has. 'You know when you have no idea what you're doing and it still goes alright? I had that today in writing. It was about fishing. I didn't understand it but it went OK.'

Tuesday 7 March

Last day before next chemo.

A really crap night last night. Night sweats and coughing at 2, and no comedy telly. Just Women's World Cup Skiing, which at least I understand, but hardly riveting. Perhaps this is just as well, as I nodded off more quickly than I had expected. At which point Tatty came to get me. 'You must be really knackered,' she said at breakfast, and I didn't disagree.

A really crappy day out there. Grey low cloud and rain, thick oily pouring wet Devon rain, with cold in it, first thing; now just incessant unsmiling endless falling drizzle, heavy, and soaking.

Came back from the school-walk, did the bins, dusted down and watched a second of *Will and Grace* and a laugh-out-loud *Frasier*, The One Where He Pretends To Be Jewish.

Felt gloomy nonetheless so decided to cheer myself up by watching our *Shakespeare in Love* DVD (I still want to say video). It was perfect, a little working stopwatch of a confection: sexy, funny and moving. What more can you want? I cried the whole way through. I don't care what they say about Gwyneth Paltrow, she can act *and* do the verse. Hoped, as it drew near to the end, that The Great Script Idea would plop into my head and make me rich *à la* Stoppard, but none did. I'll have to settle for poems.

Was reminded that it closes with William Shakespeare moving on to the next project, *Twelfth Night*, inspired by Viola's (Paltrow's) journey across the ocean. It doesn't matter that it's balls, it's a *film* for goodness sake. The dream of narrative worked for me. I might have to go onto Amazon or whatever it is and order 3 vids for £10 per month. Or even just buy some. Films I could watch now and weep a little over?

Good Will Hunting
Sliding Doors
Dead Poets Society
Truly Madly Deeply

All About My Mother
The Ice Storm
Groundhog Day

I recalled watching *Twelfth Night* at the Barbican with Mummy and Daddy all those years ago. It was one of those occasions, as I remember it, when he took us all out, with girlfriends, including a trip to Dustin Hoffman's Shylock. Somewhere I have the programmes. The bit I remember was quite early on, where Viola (Zoë Wannamaker) gives the 'cruellest she alive' speech to Olivia. It was a great double-header, sparks flashing between the pair of them, verbally and physically. The end of it isn't an important break in the play but nevertheless he clapped heavily in the pin-drop silence. I really admired him for that – going for it in the silent auditorium. It came back to me today watching Joseph Fiennes and Gwyneth Paltrow jousting and falling in love.

A lovely present from Mark today in the post. The match day programme from Chelsea/Barca from two weeks ago. His note said 'Look at the back. Do you not like the result from the Bridge?', a reference that he got Graham Taylor to sign it: 'Best wishes, Anto.' It has lovely glossy photos and expensive adverts for, among other things, *art*. A nice piece on Joe Cole (pre match-winning performance for England) on his interest in Spanish football: 'But Joe's real passion, or should that be Real passion, is going to watch them play live.' He can afford it, I suppose.

It reminded me that it came out before the death of Ossie. Peter (Carps) emailed me that day to say he saw him once with Chopper Harris and Dave Webb in a pub in Ewell and always regretted not asking for an autograph. 'He may not have played much for England, but he certainly drank for them.' I replied that watching him on telly is the reason I became a Chelsea fan. I never saw him live. 'Sometimes something comes from nowhere which makes you want to go out into a field and howl' I said. Later that night they showed him running through the Leeds defence to score that diving header, having laid off the ball just outside the centre circle. It completely did me in.

I don't think we'll win tonight. I think we'll try very hard, probably get one of the two goals we need, but will get caught on the break. I'm out of time. Time to go and get Shim from school.

I want to live.

Wednesday 8 March

Second day of chemo.

Back from hospital propped up on the bed not feeling too nauseous and rather smug. My haemoglobin has remained normal – a score of 14 – and they all love me to bits. 'I'm keen to keep the pattern of two weeks going, Tony,' Karl said, 'so if you're ready, we'll start poisoning you.'

As Lizzie, today's nurse, talked me through the side effects, he butted in loudly on entering the room with 'what's all this about a cough? You're not being male about this I hope.' He declared my chest clear and gave me '5 days, oops, seven days, slip of the pen' of antibiotics. So far so good.

Lizzie smiled when I told her about the shivery achy back pain, from the Granocyte. 'Oh that's a *good* sign,' she said. 'It means your large bones are making lots of white cells. We like that in a patient.'

There was poetry in the way Frank Keating remembered Ossie, on the back page (where else?) of the *Guardian*:

> In 1961, as sports editor of the Slough *Observer* and at a boys' cup final to present the trophy, I was riveted by a building-site tea boy, a cheery, cheeky, spindly gawk playing with a carefree dash for the winners, Old Corinthians.

Just 15, his aura of lithe grace and balance matched a bravura of power.

[. . .] I heard from his uncle Bob that my rave had helped him get a trial at Chelsea. He was, of course, Peter Osgood, the great and now, alas and so suddenly, the late. But imperishably, the smiling Old Corinthian.

Elsewhere, a nice piece on Ivor Cutler, another hero who died last week. I went to see him once, at the Bloomsbury theatre, with Dale and Mart, in our shorts and string vest phase. The gig was in support of *Gruts*, which I still have somewhere. It made me glad that I'd finally bought *Life in a Scotch Sitting Room, Vol. 2* on CD, which I think will go down as his masterpiece.

When the kids were little I used to make tapes for the car with titles like 'Everyone Happy'. The format would go something like: Smiths Song, Nursery Rhyme, Jackson 5 Song, Magic Roundabout Song, Blondie Song and so on. Once, on a whim, I included 'Episode 2' from *Life in a Scotch Sitting Room*. It became an instant family favourite, not least because it allowed us to shout 'Look! A tree!' whenever we were driving through countryside. To this day I have not seen it written down, but know large chunks by heart.

Bendy and I quoted lines of it to each other over Di's marvellous roast chicken and plum pudding meals on wheels supper:

'Down The River Clyde,' I added.
For which impertinence I received a mighty buffet, bleeding my tender nose with his vast white knuckle. How was I to know I was mouthing obscenity? But the blood soon dried and I had the pleasure of picking the clots.

What's great, on the live recording we've got, is that you can hear him losing the plot and corpsing in the pauses. Marvellous. One of my greatest achievements as a father is that Bendy has the whole album in her Ipod, and also knows most of it by heart: 'Grandma came round and scraped a lump of coarse salt onto each girl's tongue. If a fleck of spit hit you, the illusion was complete.'

Mark Radcliffe said today that Cutler's popularity make a mockery of 'youth programming', championed as he was by John Peel on late-night Radio 1. Apparently on one of his first sessions for Richard Skinner he was told to 'Take it away, Ivor!' by the DJ, only for Cutler to reply 'Take what away?' Radcliffe says, eloquently, that he was no more or less eccentric than the rest of us, only more focussed. 'He realised that you don't need to be a Renaissance man, that mastery of one thing was enough.'

Overheard on the way back from dropping Shim off today at the school gate: 'Dishwasher tablets are like gold-dust in our house.'

Thursday 9 March

A day of sudden showers, wild sunshine and breezes.

I went into work to hand in my sick note, and saw Cate and Sasha, then David in School Office. He was charming and solicitous and kept it off work and on me from the word go. He's very keen for me to carry on writing:

'If I had a diagnosis such as yours I'd be out of here. I mean, this is what I do when I'm well. I do hope you're pursuing your own work, in terms of a journal perhaps, to keep you going.'

'That's exactly what I'm doing, yes, partly as a record, partly as an act of resistance.'

'That's a huge advantage I think you have. For many in your position, and I don't mean this pejoratively, filling the time must be the most alarming aspect of the whole business because *there is nothing else*. Whereas you have a hinterland, a rich inner life which goes on. If I were you I'd be logging the progress of the journey at every opportunity.'

He almost looked jealous.

At one point he mentioned his friendship with the poet Jane Beeson. We've talked about her many times before, most recently her long 1000 line poem for the millennium in iambic pentameter. Almost as a throwaway he said he'd sent her some poems fifteen years ago, but nothing since. Recently he'd got a note from her – she has cancer too – encouraging him to send her some more. 'When are you going to get back to your writing?' she said. I left mulling on the fact that we all make choices. Even when some ghastly ones are forced upon us, deciding on who you are and what you want still has to come first.

It's also been a day of gifts. Chris Richards has sent Haruki Murakami's *Norwegian Wood* 'in case I want something a little different'; and Michèle has sent Nêuchatel poet Blaise Cendras's *Panama or the Adventures of Seven Uncles and Other Poems*, in a dual translation by John Dos Passos. Which is as 'different' again as Ian McEwan is from Kenneth Koch. They look marvellous. But they worry me. Nowhere can I find a description of what I am going through. They sit unwrapped and proud on the kitchen table, accusing me for not being able to concentrate on their wonderfulness. At least my Amazon-order of John Diamond's *C: Because Cowards get Cancer too* . . . has now arrived. I am desperate for it not to be jargon. I want to fall in love. I want it to show me me.

Later

Merenna in the bath, Shim playing White Stripes on the computer next door, Tatty with the girls in the telly room. Familiar sounds of water sloshing, guitar solos, laughter, and the heating moving bricks through the pipes. A normal evening.

Tatty reminded me of a *faux pas* in hospital yesterday while I slept on the Rituximab-Piriton cocktail. After four hours of marking children's scripts she called out to Karl behind the desk that she 'had lost the will to live.' He didn't blink apparently. On our last visit he dished out far worse himself. A very senior lady who takes up position at the other end of the ward near the telly (without switching it on) had not drawn breath all day, often having the same conversation three times over with whoever sat next to her. This isn't because she is senile. I think she is bored. And scared. And can't stop talking. After an unexpected 2-minute lull Karl went over to her chair, bent his 6' 7" frame into her sleeping face and shouted 'Geraldine, I thought you were dead there for a minute, it was so quiet. What the hell's wrong with you!' What made it even funnier was the sight of four nurses running, from different ends of the ward, to hide behind the desk, out of her eyesight, to piss themselves laughing.

Friday 10 March

Tatty said yesterday 'It's like having you with new batteries in,' referring to the post-steroid surge of energy. I stood on the scales today and reached 13 stone, for the first time in, if not years, then for at least one year. I suppose lack of cycling plus ravenous hunger all the time can only lead to one thing. Another cake today, from Guy and Jemima round the corner. Clearly word has got round. 'It's one of Carol's,' he said. 'We don't bake and anyway she's a genius.' He's not wrong there, a lemon sponge of the lightest consistency, oozing jam and cream. Cancer-benefit Number 34: women *buy* you cakes and send them round with their husbands.

Tatty brought up the issue of Chelsea losing so late in the day on Wednesday that I think Karl forgot to be scornful. Maybe the rule is we only slag each other's teams off in the mornings. He said he didn't watch the game as he was at 'my nerdy geologist meeting in Cornwall.'
    'What, you study rocks?'
    'Oh yes, and collect them.'
    'What, like, in little boxes with labels in display cases.'
    'Yes, in little boxes with labels in display cases.'
    'And you travel all over for rock samples?'

'Yup. Cornwall's especially good. Was up in St Just the other day with my mate Rick and suddenly his Geiger counter goes off the scale. And it just looked like a brown bit of rock, so we smash it open and there it is, perfect specimen of radon. He took one half, I took the other. Made a special lead box for it and stuck it in the roof. Week later I realised radon is heavier than air, and it was right above my head, where I'd put it. What you need is a big airy loft, one of those big houses.'

John Diamond's *C* has arrived from Amazon. In his intro he tackles the issue of war-metaphor head-on. I was right. I was sure I had read this before, in one of his *Times* pieces. At the risk of using another useless war metaphor where none will do, he blows the whole idea of 'fighting' cancer apart:

> My antipathy to the language of battles and fights has nothing to do with pacifism and everything to do with a hatred for the sort of mortality which says that only those who fight hard against their cancer survive it – the corollary being that those who lose the fight deserved to do so.

Saturday 14 March

To Northwood, to see Mummy and Daddy and everyone else. We drove up last evening, after Tats had been to Hayley for her hair. Hayley has given me a free treatment with her friend who is an 'Intuitive Holistic Therapist . . . Bringing Mind, Body and Spirit Together (Body Massage, Hot Stone Massage, Reiki, Chakra, Crystal and Colour Healing: Available soon . . . Aromotherapy and Reflexology May 2006).' She read me the blurb as we sped up the M4: 'Reiki is the natural life force energy that lives and breathes within and all around us, without it we cannot exist,' at which point I asked her to stop. 'Hot stone massage sounds nice,' she said.

'What is it?'

'They put hot stones on you.'

'Right.'

'But it's got to be better than reflexology. Touching your feet, euggh,' she said.

We wolfed sausage casserole and baked potatoes with cole-slaw, tomato salad and cheese. The kind of meal you dream awaits you when you enter the house of your birth. Mart popped round and hugged me heavily in the doorway. We talked about cycling into DK on The Strand each day, the kind of gear he needs and prefers. 'As long as it's Gore-Tex you're all right,' he frowned. He's sold one piece from last week's private show, lots of enquiries for others.

Once Tats had gone up with the kids we got down to it a bit more, but not really. He didn't like the photos we'd sent of my shaving ceremony. 'I found it shocking to be honest,' he said. 'It brought it all home.'

Shim was sick today at breakfast. He still isn't right, really, a shadow of his usual bounce and energy. He spent most of the morning watching the last ever episode of *Dick and Dom in Da Bungalow*, under a rug, with a little red bowl to be sick in again if he needed to be. It's exactly the same sick bowl I used to be given thirty years ago. Tats, who 'does not do sick' gingerly went with him to the loo while he went through the worst of it. 'Did you hear me flushing each time? Incredibly brave if you ask me,' and I knew she meant herself, not Shim.

Meanwhile I sat with Mummy and Daddy in the kitchen eating cold toast and taking the last fistfuls of drugs. I drew them little diagrams to explain the layout of the ward, then wrote down the names of the drugs I'm given, the ones I've learned at least. Rituximab (the R of R-CHOP) came first; then cyclophosphamide (which just screams poison), the C of CHOP; then Vincristine (which is the O of CHOP under another name). (I expect R-CHVP is much more of a mouth-ful than R-CHOP, sounding like a suburb of Gdansk, or a Russian submarine port, plus you don't get the irony of the word 'chop', because this cancer treatment involves no surgical intervention at all.)

I explained the process to them for the first time. There's the one that makes your bottom itchy; the one that looks (and makes you pee) like Ribena; the one that makes a cold burning ache up your arm; the one which is syrupy and takes twice as long to squirt into you.

'Is it on a drip?' they said.

'Through a cannula, on a saline drip.'

'How do you spell that?' said Daddy.

I spelled it for him.

'And they leave it in all day?'

'All day.'

'You must be shattered.'

'What's the worst part?' said Mummy.

'The half hour when you get home of not being sure if you're going to throw up.'

Have been enjoying my John Diamond. It reads, as they say, like a thriller, even though you know the outcome already. Propped up in bed last night with it a little bookmark fell out the back, one I hadn't noticed when I unwrapped it from its parcel. It turns out I ordered it from a Used and New seller called Killer Books. Of course I did. How appropriate.

Monday 13 March

What is having cancer like? You think that you'll spend the morning finally getting down to discovering what 'East Coker' is about, or re-reading *Life Studies*, or Isaiah; then spend the afternoon in contemplation of Tarkovsky's *Nostalgia* before picking the children up from school, pausing on the way home for a hot chocolate with whipped cream. Instead you encounter three people on the way home, each of them stopping to ask how you are while their child pulls on their coat behind them. You assure them you feel fine. In truth, you are cold and feel tired to your bones. All you want to do is run – run! – home and watch *Will and Grace* and *Frasier* reruns. You watch the traffic very carefully, only crossing when it is safe. You watch the *Will and Grace* and *Frasier* reruns, savouring every embarrassment, every excess of linguistic frippery, determined to repeat them to your loved ones when they return home. You have a marvellous time, hearing your laughter in an empty home, nothing outside but the wind. Five minutes later, during a documentary programme on T-shirt sellers at Camden Lock, you realise you cannot remember a syllable of the dialogue, an iota of the plot. How ironic: you have longed for whole days like this, left to your own devices, no toys to tidy, no child batting the tent of your newspaper every ten seconds, and you cannot concentrate on a thing, even the T-shirt sellers of Camden Lock. A colleague emails to say they will call first and bring cake. They do neither. Instead, a friend rings up saying he has made you a rap CD. He brings it round and you listen to it, sipping tea. You tell stories about your children and when they were ill. Somehow this makes you feel better.

Tuesday 14 March

Not one of my best days.

I notice, just writing the date down, that it is a month since we went to see Felicity Carr. Amazing how routine illness can become. The routine I'm now settled into seems inescapable, repeating itself through the side effects like a series of well-placed dominoes falling one after the other in one of those record-breaking attempts on children's television: 5 days of Radioactive Man, followed by 7 of Completely Shattered Man, followed by 2 of Almost-Back-To-Normal Man, at which point, it starts again.

When did I get this?

Was it there on Christmas Day as I carved the turkey wearing my lovely stripy shirt given to me for my anniversary? Yes.

Was it there when I played football two days after Christmas and got bollocked by Pug's friend Tristan because I was slow, useless, had no first touch and let in three quick goals? Yes. Was it there when I cooked chicken with lemon and olives for my students? Yes. Was it there when I struggled into work a week later feeling fluey and everyone said kindly how terrible I looked? Yes. It was there when I burned CDs from the library and it was there when I lit fireworks in the garden for the kids. It was there when I went to the dump with Shim and it was there when Bendy and I shopped in the January sales. It was there at Boston Tea Party, over latte, and it was there at the family curry. It was there when I cycled to work and it was there when I strolled round the quay. It was there when I emailed colleagues and it was there when I sent apologies to meetings. It was there when I lectured students and there when we met 1:1. It was there in my initials in their files. It was there when I went for bread, when I made love, bought cheese, scanned the sports pages, picked up a poetry book, posted a postcard, had my haircut, made porridge, called the builder.

It was there, uninvited and growing, in the dark. I did not ask for it. I did not deserve it. It is not fair. But it found me, and I accepted it.

Later

That phrase. *It isn't fair.* Apparently it's what Gabe said to Misty when I had emailed her with the news. 'He's never hurt anyone, that man,' as though that makes it more injurious. Apart from showing that Gabe doesn't know me that well, the logic, while instant, is all too terrifying. It is as though there are men and women down the road from me far more deserving of cancer because of their careers in crime or tendencies towards bullying at school. Or, to put it another way, that I am less 'deserving' of cancer than someone with a bit of a cruel streak in them or who knocks their kids about. It's preposterous. It both isn't fair and has nothing to do with

70

fairness at all. It isn't a competition I entered for secretly then forgot about: 'Bad luck, Mr Wilson, your numbers came up this week. Bet you thought you'd cancelled your subscription. Well, it's still running, and you've been chosen as this week's winner.'

It just happens. And if I live and recover, as everyone keeps saying they are certain I will, that has nothing to do with fairness either. It doesn't make me a better 'fighter' of the disease if I survive; or a weaker, weedier person if I don't. It just means the treatment will work for me, or it won't. Of course I want to live. But I don't want anyone saying within a mile of me that it's unfair I got it. It's unfair on everyone who gets it, if it is at all. I'd rather say 'tough' as in 'it's tough for every person who has it' and just leave it at that. Just as it is good if you recover – though 'good' will never adequately cover it – and very tough if you don't. Though that doesn't cover it either. Let's say a Kray twin, or Hitler, they get it, then die. I know they'd feel they had just as much right to 'conquer it' as I do. And according to Gabe, I never hurt anyone. Little does he know.

Wednesday 15 March

My hair – such as it is – started falling out today. I was sitting in the bath when I noticed it. A faint grey scum just above the water level. On closer inspection it was made up of tiny, 3½ millimetres, say, strands of hair. It reminded me of what my bathwater used to look like the day after a visit to the barber's as a boy. I called out to Tats and she came in and confirmed it. When she went back to the bedroom to fix my syringes I pinched hard on my scalp. They were there, too, at the end of my finger, lifeless iron filings that, because of their size, seemed heavy and fragile at the same time. It is very odd seeing it 'go' at last. It's not like I leave great clumps of it lying around (though if you look hard enough you can see it on my pillow), nor that huge discs of pink appear on my scalp where there were none before. I have lived with the prospect of it 'going' for ten years or so, since a short haircut became a necessity, not a question of fashion. But now that it is falling out for real I find I mourn its passing, in spite of the pre-emptive haircut with the boys, and in spite of the compliments from women (the main difference between men and women? Women say 'Don't you look gorgeous!'. Men say: 'You never had much to lose anyway'). It is one more sign of the process taking hold, one little step further away from looking (and feeling) like the person I was before I had cancer.

Racing through the final pages of Diamond. It will be a loss when he goes/when I finish. I like his logician's mind very much:

> It's the idea of taking spiritual responsibility for a disease once it's been diagnosed which annoys me. For it leads to the idea of the survivor as personal hero that only those who want to survive enough get through to the end, and the implied corollary that those who die are somehow lacking in moral fibre and the will to live.

There's another lovely bit where he's listening to the usual suspects on some 'jocular' Radio 4 programme, where they have to work out the medieval recipe for quince jelly by following some sort of Sanskrit riddle, and he hears the old him for the first time. I love the very real double take here, but also the idea that the pre-cancer Diamond seems to have no idea what is about to hit him:

> He was the one who didn't realise what a boon an unimpaired voice was, who ate his food without stopping to think about its remarkable flavour, who was criminally profligate with words, who took his wife and children and friends for granted – in short who didn't know he was living.

It really does take a special book – a book about dying – to make you notice your life more closely.

I must have seen twenty people today. First James Bradley came round for coffee, then half an hour later Linda Southwood. She brought daffs (as did James) and a stick of French bread from Tesco's. 'I found that the one thing I wanted to be friends with was this,' she said, handing it to me. 'You read my mind,' I said.

She recounted comedy-howlers from her own chemo-days: a child, concerned she was overdoing it by constantly receiving visitors, saying 'Mummy, you should really be upstairs dying'; another child, admonishing her for eating his burnt-toast-crusts: 'Don't! They're carcinogenic!'

Then I went to the pub to see Group S who were celebrating the end of the taught course with chips and a lager. For the third time that day I heard myself holding court and describing the steroid energy-rush followed by the Granocyte-induced-crash. 'You look bloody good on it anyway,' said one. I'm learning to say thank you to this, on the grounds that it is much nicer to be told you look well (even if it is a lie) than it is to be told you look worn out in the name of honesty.

They were on good form, demob-happily passing on gossip about other groups and students, including at least two course-couples I have taught and had no idea about. Apparently one student called her classroom assistant a lesbian on day one of her teaching practice, then couldn't understand why the staffroom sent her to Coventry.

I ate a plate of chips, sipped my mineral water, and felt normal for an hour.

On the way out I took a pre-emptive Paracetamol to counter the shooting pains in my back, a repeat, almost to the hour, of how I felt last week. As Tatty says, the Granocyte may keep me alive, but apart from the nausea on the night of my treatments, it is the side effect I have come to dread the most.

On the way I saw Cara and Gina in the deli buying sandwiches – on the way to see me. We sat round the kitchen table. For the first time in months I heard some work-gossip (all of mine is stuck at December 2005, an eon ago) and felt both relieved to be away from it all and alienated at the same time.

I queued in Lloyds the Chemist behind some ladies and their prescriptions. While we stood there in silence – a waiting room kind of silence, for a shop – I began to listen to the inane chatter of the in-house radio station, Lloyds FM. It's the sort of thing Jimmy Young used to do on Radio Two ('In a minute, your calls on bowel cancer, meanwhile, here's Abba') except it is entirely about health, unleavened by politics or showbiz or sport.

As I listened I learned that there is a shortage of radiologists in the UK. Dr Martin someone from the Royal College of Radiologists (is there one for everything?) was explaining that we just aren't making enough of them, hence the waiting lists all over the country for people to receive CT and ultrasound scans. Hence the relief in the GP's face when, on January 20th, my pain undiminished, I asked if, well, he wouldn't mind recommending me for a private scan. 'I was just about to suggest the same to you,' he sighed. 'Normally I'm reluctant as I never know how people will react. But in your case it's a good idea. In any case you wouldn't have been seen for another six weeks, even on the urgent list.'

Friday 17 March

'What are the side effects like?' friends ask.

'Do you really want to know?'

They blink.

The main one they've heard about – the main one I had heard about until just over a month ago – is the sickness. This is the one, my performance on the first evening of chemo excepted, that I seem to have escaped most conspicuously. Tatty and the children will tell you, however, that I seem to burp constantly ('Dad, that really smells!') and that every time I do I feel as though I might be about to throw up. I haven't –yet– but for that one night, but it feels as though I've reached the point of no return, every time.

So I don't tell them about that, referring instead, expert that I now am, to 'the cycle.'

'It must be very tiring,' they say.

They are not joking.

This is all to generalise, though.

I've noticed subtle shifts in the side effects from cycle 1 to cycle 2, although the general pattern remains just as I have described it.

Cycle 1 side effects:

1. Night 1. Threw up. Felt sick even afterwards. Felt sick next day but wasn't.
2. Experienced the energy rush for the first time. Went into town and ate pizza. Felt:
   I can do this.
3. Very poor sleep patterns. Woke 3 days in a row with an axe-through-the-head-post-drinking-days headache.
4. Constipation.
5. Then diarrhoea.
6. Then diarrhoea again.
7. A tickly cough leading to lack of sleep. Also leading, or contributing to
8. Extreme, hit-with-a-cricket-bat, fatigue.
9. Shivers and shakes and backache.
10. Shivers and shakes and backache.

Cycle 2 side effects:

1. Felt sick. Wasn't. Felt smug.
2. Mad energy rush. Went into work to hand in sick note (they all said how well I looked).
3. Got rid of cough (mostly). Slept.

4. Almost to the hour, the return of the fatigue on the Tuesday after (hereafter known as the Tuesday After).
5. Muscle ache: back of legs, and in lower right arm.
6. Diarrhoea.
7. More diarrhoea.
8. Even more diarrhoea.
9. Achy back (no shivers and shakes).
10. Return of the night sweats.
11. Hair loss, including beard.

Rich called and described in more detail than I wish I could remember his wee: 'At night a Burgundy, in the morning a rich Bordeaux' (he has kidney stones).

We talked about people praying for us. 'It's beginning to bounce off me a little,' he said. 'I mean, I know they mean it, but, partly it is something to say, to take up the space at the end of a card or phone call. I mean what they don't say is 'I am expecting the living God of the Universe to reach into your pain and bless you with his healing touch.'

'It's a bit long for a start,' I said.

'So instead they say, "I'll pray for you."'

Somehow I found this tremendously encouraging. It turns out he's just been given *Blue Like Jazz*. I told him to cut to the chase and go to the bit on cancer and war metaphor.

Monday 20 March

A real curiosity in the post this morning: a card, book (*The Maker's Diet: The creator's plan for optimal health!*), leaflet and *Healing Scriptures* CD from the mother of a friend. It took me a whole minute of looking at her name before realising who it was bombarding me with unasked-for Christian material.

I did not find it helpful. Something about the syntax in sentence 1 of the card aroused my suspicion straight away: 'I was so sorry to hear about the cancer.' It isn't that it is ungrammatical, it is that it isn't true. What I mean is that it acknowledges my having cancer without really communicating any sorrow that I have it. It's all in that word 'the'. 'I was so sorry to hear about the cancer.' Not: 'that you have cancer'; not: 'that you have been diagnosed with cancer'; not even the euphemistic: 'about your illness.' Instead: 'about the cancer.' Just: the cancer. Not 'your cancer' but '*the* cancer'. Placing it, *the* cancer, in a kind of possessive-less limbo, as though not attached to or, dare I say it, living in an actual human being, thereby acknowledging its presence, but not acknowledging me. Which is, ironically, to deny both the cancer, with its determined determiner 'the', and me at the same time.

The leaflet made me shudder as well: 'sickness, disease, pain, I resist you in the name of Jesus. You are not the will of God. I enforce the Word of God on you. I will not tolerate you in my life. My days of sickness and disease are over!' (I've just looked back at the prayers either side of this and three out of four of them close with an exclamation mark, too.) Apart from the fact that the days of my disease are not (yet) over; and apart from the war metaphor (enforcing the Word of God); it is the triumphalistic tone of this which I find so unappealing. Imagine you are an old lady being given this by an enthusiastic new vicar; or a man who has just discovered secondaries on his lung, having been clear for three years: what are you supposed to feel if you do not share the leaflet-writer's certainty that you are cured? Where does this kind of thing leave you? People of faith are made to feel worse by this kind of thing, through the guilt that it induces a) for not getting better, if that happens and b) anxiety and fear for not having 'resisted' hard enough. I know my friend's mother means well, and I know I should be grateful, but I only find it depressing, rather as I find double glazing salesman who ring you during supper depressing. Of course I want to get better, but I am not going to pray prayers that I can't subscribe to culturally or, for want of a better word, linguistically. It reminds me of what I remember one writer saying in a *Guardian* piece from last year: 'Truth starts with syntax.' This leaflet is not true.

I opened the book, very warily, at random. In a chapter which is a long list of 'Don'ts' entitled 'How to Get Sick: A Post Modern Prescription for Illness' we are entreated (no. 23) not to 'Use plastic food storage products, the popular food wraps [nor] re-use plastic drinking bottles,' 'Do aerobic exercise' (no. 17) and 'Get tattoos' (no. 10). No. 20, where I opened the page, warns against the dangers of wearing tight underclothing:

> Lymph nodes that are compressed or blocked by tight underclothing such as bras or other tight clothing may not allow the lymph system to be properly cleansed. [. . .] Women should not wear bras to bed.

I am so glad I knew that.

Back at the card which accompanies all this, the penultimate line reads 'Trust Tatti (sic) & the children are all doing well.' Poor spelling aside, this rather falls between the two stools of thoughtfulness (she remembers that I am not alone and that my cancer has affected all of us) and naïve optimism (on what grounds is that (person-free) trust based? Has she spoken to my consultant?). It is also horribly informal. It is 'Trust that . . .' not that 'I trust that . . .'. This is a person I have not seen for over three years and she is writing to me as though we chatted for half an hour on the phone last night.

I haven't unwrapped my *Healing Scriptures* CD from its plastic sheath yet. The blurb on the back opens with: 'Defeat your doubts and receive your healing by allowing the healing power of God's word to flow through you.' This assumes a) I have doubts about God's power/love, b) that I am not allowing him to heal me, the inference of which is that I am to blame and c) that if I don't defeat my doubts (more war metaphor) I'll be in a lot of trouble. The CD promises, furthermore, to '[give] you powerful promises to stand on for healing.' I'm sorry, but what does 'stand on for healing' mean?

Does it mean 'go on standing', with the implication that I may have to stand for some time before being healed, i.e. that it will involve lots of *effort* and hard work on my part; or does it mean, simply, to stand *for* healing? Which begs the question, why 'stand' for healing and not 'sit' or 'collapse on the sofa for healing' or 'have a lie down', which is what I feel like most of the time. Why do I pick up a dreadful whiff of testosterone-fuelled muscular-Christianity from all of these products? And why do so many of us, the mothers of friends included, fall for it?

Later

Have spent the day feeling coldy and tired and demotivated. Watched with huge relief the return, post-Cheltenham Festival, of *Will and Grace* and *Frasier*. The *Will and Grace* I watch, as I always do, in awe of the comic timing and delighting in the sugary overdose of it all. The *Frasier* was The One Where Niles Hires A Lawyer.

I moved on to the Commonwealth Games, but found I cried though most of it. This is partly because athletics always makes me cry; but I found it happened with the swimming as well. A boy from Exeter has his just won back-to-back silver and now gold in the backstroke. He went, at one time, to Tats' school, and the swimming club the kids used to go to. 'He'll have been shouted at by that bloke in the tracksuit like you were,' I enthused, but they didn't seem impressed.

Didn't really settle to very much. Made a plan to take CDs back to the library, but felt too tired, plus, it is still freezing.

Got a call from nowhere from Bex. She came round later for tea and we nattered over the kitchen table good-naturedly for an hour or so. I went back over the story with her. In one sense it is very old news, old hat, even; in another I cannot believe it is happening to me.

Less Brian Eno today, more of a Syd Barrett, in truth. The post-Floyd, living-with-his-mother-in-Cambridge Barrett:

not really a shining crazy diamond, but a slightly overweight middle-aged bloke looking haunted.

Of course, you still slip into war metaphor when you're not thinking. I saw Vince across the road walking back from dropping of Shim. He called out how are you and I called back: 'Fighting off a cold.' 'But you've nothing to fight it off with!' he shouted.

Tuesday 21 March

First day of Spring, last day before chemo no. 3.

Spent the morning shuffling round the house and blubbing watching the Commonwealth Games. I found the slightest thing set me off, from the former-pupil of Tatty's school gaining another backstroke record, to the sight of two Kenyan women dominating the 10,000 metres, crossing themselves in ecstasy as they reached the finishing line. Ray came round looking concerned, having spoken to Lucinda who saw me venturing out for fruit as she swept her hedge clippings yesterday. I told him there was nothing he could do, but thanks. I went back into the kitchen to empty the dishwasher then cried all the way through a CD.

At the post office a very odd parcel from Mandy Coe was waiting for me – half a dozen 'hard-boiled eggs' in an egg box in bubblewrap. They aren't real eggs, but nor are they chocolate. I licked one. They are definitely sugar-coated. She says she found them in Suffolk in breaks from workshopping with teachers – one of the gigs I have given up this year. 'Do you remember these from childhood?' she says. I don't. But they are so odd they cheered me up no end.

As did her letter. She's got friends and family 'who've met cancer' and gets it exactly right: 'with just one test or diagnosis you find yourself slipping through a thin partition and suddenly you are outside your old world.' She says you live somewhere for years, noticing the Ethel Austin and the chip shop, but not the cancer support centre. And it's just as near to your house. How true.

Her other brilliant image is about the treatment. 'Imagine your body is an island,' she says, '(not Man or Dogs). There is just one leaf on one tree that's a bit brown round the edges. And they use a hurricane to blow it away.' That nails it for me better than anything I've seen by anyone. She's busy preparing a poetry Ms, she says. On this form, she should have no trouble.

Later

I handed Bendy and Tats a hard-boiled egg each before supper. They immediately started licking them, then whacking them on the coffee table. Bendy got hers to open first. 'Yum, chocolate! Incredibly sugary, but great.' So now I know. Proof that Mandy was more spoiled as a child than I was. I had thought they were *papier-mâché* and for painting.

Wednesday March 22

Third chemo day.

A quiet day on the ward today: it must have been, as we started a whole hour later and got home at the same time. Or maybe they think I'm built like an ox and just blast me through it in double-quick time.

Nadine did my injections again. She has huge dark brown eyes and is very smiley. 'I'll stop gassing in a minute and you can sleep,' she said, injecting me with Piriton.

We nattered about the drugs like they were fashion accessories. 'So I know the "C" and the "O" which is really a "V", I said, trying to impress her, 'but which is the "H"?'

'Technically there isn't an H at all,' she said.

'Which means it'd be R-COP instead?'

'I guess once they thought of CHOP they couldn't lose it. It kept them amused I guess.'

'Do you do other chemo regimes?'

'Oh yes. There's one called FLAG I do. And FLAG IDA.'

'They must have such fun dreaming them up.'

'Gives them something to do, I suppose.'

She asked how Tatty was and about the kids.

'They're amazing, considering,' I said, repeating what I must have said a hundred times in the last two weeks. I warmed to my theme: 'They're very matter of fact about it, really. If they want to talk about it, we do and if they don't we don't. We don't not use the word cancer around them, though. It's important to be straightforward.'

'Absolutely, I'm sure you're right.'

It struck me as the word cancer popped out of my mouth that until then the ward was the only place I'd not heard it used. At the school gate, in the bedroom, round the kitchen table, on street corners, but never on the ward itself.

'If we do have a moment it's usually deferred angst,' Tatty chipped in.

"Where's-my-jumper-I'm-late-Dad!' kind of thing,' I said. 'Homework is a good one too.'

Nadine laughed.

'Apparently Shimi's best friend from school asked him how it was going and all he said was, "We get baked lots of cakes." Who's to say that's not important to him?'

Very little sleep last night, which I spent most of on the sofa. Not from nerves but from this dreadful cough I can't seem to shake off. They're taking it seriously, giving me a codeine-based cough mixture and more (and stronger this time) antibiotics.

At around twelve I woke up spluttering as usual and shuffled into the TV room. I couldn't bring myself to switch it on; it would only have been women's bowls or the 50m trap shooting.

Thursday 23 March

A lovely morning lying around in the bedroom with Tatty, who has finally been signed off. We nattered and cuddled and I brought her fennel tea and cereal. Then into town for banking errands, buying a mop for the cleaners, and booking in a Specsavers visit for Tats. Then lunch (on the sofas!) at BTP. Yummy avocado salad sandwich (why do I crave this?) and a toasted melty looking panini for T. Cosiness. We flicked through a hi-fi/electronics mag and fantasised over Roberts Digital Radios. 'Why don't you get one for your birthday?' she said. 'You'll be getting lots of money.' Suddenly realised in my bones that I am extremely materialistic, wanting not only a DAB radio but a Howies cycling jacket and Ipod as well. She took me to Fat Face and had success choosing a top and a beanie 'from the kids'. Found myself lusting over a pair of loafers in the Bally window on the way back. Felt slightly cross with myself.

A freezing raw day to be out and about in. But good. Bumped into Will across the road carrying a large plank of wood for a job round the corner. First time we've really stopped to chat recently, so I told him. Not at my most fluent, to be honest. When he asked how I was I said 'Well, not great actually, well, worse than that. I've been diagnosed with cancer.' So I told him the story (I've got pretty good at condensing it into four sentences) and he frowned and was terribly sweet. I'm still telling people for the first time: Kathryn Heyman, on email ('Oh God. I can't – can I call you?'); then Claire the Advisory Teacher on the walk back from school: 'Oh God, what, really?'

Saturday 25 March

At the school gate yesterday I saw Fiona.

'God, you look awful.'

'No, the correct response is "You look really well, Anthony."'

'Sorry. But you do.'

'Well, that's OK, because I feel dreadful.'

'Oh no, what is it?'

'Streaming cold. Constant coughing fits at night. No sleep. Apart from that I'm fine.'

'Look, if there's *anything* I can do.'

'Absolutely, we'll let you know.'

'You look like you've put on weight actually.'

'Well spotted. I have. They said not to worry about calorie intake.'

'Because I saw you the other day and thought you looked heavier, you know, in the face. Do you know when it started? Perhaps it was last year with your job hanging in the air, because you were really low then weren't you?'

'They said they don't know. But it's aggressive, so it's probably very recent.'

'At least that means they can hit it aggressively though, doesn't it?'

'Absolutely.'

'Look, when are you going to come round, would you like to come round?'

'Love to.'

'OK, I'll call you.'

'OK, call us, that'd be great.'

I bet she won't.

Later we went to book group and everyone was lovely. Possibly too lovely. Tom Nicolas called across the room 'You look very sexy.' When I said thank you I'll take that as a compliment he went 'I didn't *mean* it as a compliment,' and sniffed.

Tom Lloyd whispered to me what Lucinda said when I walked in: 'It's not fair, he's even better looking than he is when he has hair.' 'But I don't suppose she actually told you that, did she?'

We did have a good comparing notes session, though. She said how people always were reminding her to 'be positive' and how if she did that she'd have a better chance. 'But I never worked out what they meant. Because I would only be able to think of every negative thing. It was the people who came up to me and dealt with it head-on and asked how I felt that I might die who I liked the best.'

I explained I'd been reading the John Diamond. He took it to mean: 'Be positive when you're around me.' She laughed at this. 'But it's funny,' she went on, 'you find yourself overcompensating for and protecting people, even as you tell them, making sure they can handle it. It's what we do.'

The day began with a classic, multi-orifice explosion at 5 am. I sat on the loo and felt desolate. Outside, forlorn birdsong. I thought of Patrick Kavanagh's 'Wet Evening in April':

> The birds sang in the wet trees
> And as I listened to them it was a hundred years from now
> And I was dead and someone else was listening to them.
> But I was glad I had recorded for him the melancholy.

I don't know if I have said this, but I absolutely loathe and detest having cancer. Something about the wretchedness of unstoppable coughing and simultaneous diarrhoea, combined with a ten-tissue-per-half-hour cold just got to me yesterday. I just couldn't see the funny side – my beard rubbing off in my hand! – any more. I feel bloated, lethargic, overweight, slumped. And everyone, Fiona aside, says how marvellous I look. Which is lovely, even if they *are* lying. The downside is that I don't have permission to say how guilty I feel. I heard myself on the phone talking to Mummy and Daddy and for the first time in ages the perkiness had gone. I was all monosyllables, in between splutters. I could hear Mummy getting more upset at 'being so far away' but there was nothing I could do to disguise it. I felt terrible. Then guilty for letting them know it. Then slightly annoyed that they sounded surprised. Then guilty again. So it goes on.

Jay called earlier with his familiar 'Allo, cancer-boy' greeting.

He toned it down a bit when I answered by way of coughing for half a minute into the mouthpiece. Sometimes I would like to punch him.

The most touching thing of all? Phil from the greengrocer's (aka The World's Most Grumpy Man) gave me his number this morning and said 'Young man, I've two friends who've had treatment like yours. If you're not up to coming out just call us and we'll bring it round. You're only round the corner, aren't you?' I had only told Jen out of the team. Now I am under each of their wings. I just stood there saying 'How amazingly kind, thank you' like a proverbial stuck record. Then the punchline: '£12.20, young man. To you, £12.'

Monday 27 March

A better night, with only one-minor-coughing fit, at around half-one. Then diarrhoea at four, then again at six. Lay awake in between, listening to my plumbing. Read large chunks of the *Guardian* Saturday Review while sitting there, including a piece about Michael Holroyd having bowel cancer. He's looking forward to the time when he can look back on it and say it's all over. It's funny how cancer suddenly attaches itself to the minutiae of the day. Alex from *Neighbours* has just died from a 'rare form of lymphoma', leaving Susan and his kids to fend for themselves. And this morning the radio was full of the woman from Swindon who has taken her NHS Healthcare Trust to the Appeal Court so she can get treated with Herceptin, the 'miracle' breast cancer drug. In the lead-up to her story they played interviews with other cancer sufferers, notably a very articulate 26-year-old woman with liver cancer, recently refused another wonder-drug which would have reduced the tumour by 4 cm and therefore made it operable. 'What did you feel when the treatment was denied to you?' she was asked. 'Despair,' she said simply.

While Tatty walked Shim to school and went for a walk I

watched back-to-back doubles of *Will and Grace* and *Frasier*. The One Where Grace Doesn't Get Engaged, followed by The One Where Frasier Sees Off a Rival Shrink On Air. Tats joined me for the last bit of the latter and we giggled on the sofa together. OK, except it tends to start off my crying.

I stepped outside briefly to move the car later and on the way back up the road saw Lawrence. He was in his car. He pulled over, got out and hugged me like the prodigal son. He didn't flinch when I didn't try to pretend that things had not been going well recently. 'Any time of the day or night, if you want to come over and talk, or not talk, you're always welcome, you know that,' he said. I have only just realised the strength that comes from admitting that this is a hard time. Not 'strength' exactly, but some kind of peace, perhaps. Or rather, just an absence of guilt, a lack of worry about protecting people's feelings. It still feels risky, though.

Tuesday 28 March

A day of racing clouds, squally winds and wince-inducing sunlight. Temperature climbing at last and buds starting to show on the lilac tree.

Have felt completely energy-less all day. Grounded; beached. The aerial man came at nine and I spent half an hour not understanding a word he said except that it will cost £170 to go digital. Watched some perfect-timing *Frasier* with Tats, then went to bed and slept till lunch.

Had woken only once during the night, around half-one, not coughing that seriously. Found myself jumping out of bed with unseemly energy at half-six for the (usual) diarrhoea, which lasted longer than ever before. I wept, silently.

Have felt on the verge of throwing up all day, without ever really feeling sick – if that makes sense. A tenderness in the waters, in the absolute base of who you are, that it's all about to go up (or down) and that it will hurt.

A lovely package in the post today from Wes: a spanking Howies woollen hat 'to fend off the interminable cold.'

Thursday 30 March

Went to hospital yesterday and spent the morning dozing on the ward. Was in just to get a top-up of antibiotics, but they give you the full service and MOT, whatever. Bloods, blood pressure, temperature, check-up, chat. Karl strode around croaking sounding worse than me, though I couldn't tell if this was from watching Arsenal beat Juventus the night before. In the end I didn't dare ask.

They seemed certain that the constant diarrhoea is due to the strength of the antibiotics 'stripping my stomach of good bacteria', as Charlotte, my doctor, put it. They gave me two pots to fill with sample fluids. Felt pretty demoralised on my return – despite the blood levels being 'normal' – and sat waiting for a colleague to come and take me out for pizza with the students.

I was glad I went, though exhausted by it nevertheless. On entering the restaurant and seeing them all sitting there I realised how nervous I was, not of them, but of sitting in a crowd of people and having to perform and be jolly. Suddenly felt very afraid. Partly because I'm croaky, snotty and coughing and partly because I wondered if I'd have anything to say which wasn't related to being ill. They were very sweet, taking me through the gossip from the course rather like adult children, arms interlocked, guiding an elderly parent round a stately home garden.

I noticed I ate for England, wolfing my pizza and mixed salad.

I bought Liv a bunch of lilies to say thank you for taking over the running of the course and she looked genuinely surprised and grateful, still managing to say that she wished it had been a pleasure. I let it go, as I did her quip about being well enough to do some second marking. As I had predicted to myself, she congratulated me on my 'lovely shaped head'.

Went out for lunch today as well. At 12 Tatty looked up and said 'Let's go to Dart's Farm.' We picked up Ellie on the way and had a very bright time. They both had the steak with pepper sauce ('and yesterday's vegetables': T) and I went for the proverbial sausage, mash and onion gravy. A nice Dijon mustard as well. Great comfort food. At one point Ellie and I got out our pills together. It turns out she took the same antibiotic whilst in hospital recently.

'Did it give you diarrhoea?'

'Yes. Dreadfully.'

'How long did it take to go?'

'Well, I finished the course on Sunday and I still have it now.'

'Poor old you.'

'And it was black for some reason.'

'One thing I will say is how good I've got at swallowing pills.'

'You're an amateur. I've had loads more practice.'

'Ellie, I am *so* sorry, that was unbelievably tactless of me.'

She didn't flinch. 'It's no problem. I can do up to 30.'

'In one go?'

'Oh, yes.'

'My record's about six.'

'Pathetic,' she grinned.

Afterwards I went out like a recalcitrant child to the car and slept while they pootled and did some shopping. It's amazing, this urge to sleep nearly all the time; and to eat, too. On the one hand I'm surprised I haven't lost more weight, with the diarrhoea; on the other hand I can't understand why I'm not a complete porker. I walk with a wheezy old-man shuffle, and am breathless going up stairs, while feeling compelled to put sweet things in my mouth at regular intervals in between meals, not all of them apples and bananas. Another level of weirdness regarding this is that I still step onto the scales each day (as I used to before being ill) in the same kind of antic-ipatory hope, as though by finding out that I am less than 13 stone I can suddenly predict or look forward to a run of good health. Yet I don't really want to lose weight at all. My before-cancer brain very much wants me to, not least so I can start wearing my slimmer-fitting trousers again. But my rational mind knows that weight loss is a symptom of NHL. By going for the 'trio of sausages' (with apple tart for afters) I am, Canute-like, ordering the waves to recede a little. That I feel bloated with it only confuses the hard-drive when I'm told by everyone (students, the school gate) that I look so well.

With the sample-pots, yesterday, a little chit in a plastic bag with my details on. They use stickers for the repeated stuff (name, DOB, hospital no., etc.), but there, in black and white, and very legible, a summary of my cancer in the top right hand corner: 'High-grade B cell diffuse NHL.' It was seeing the words 'high-grade' which got me. Somehow seeing it written down seemed to make it more or less official. After all, I've received no letter telling me I have this disease. Seeing 'high-grade', code for 'aggressive', next to the abbreviated NHL, made my particular form of the cancer all the more serious, suddenly.

Friday 31 March

A day of comings and goings. The telly man came and did our aerial this morning, so now we have digital TV, much to the children's delight. If I'm careful I could watch 'old' telly all day now. The box we have has all sorts of things I've never paid attention to before: something called ITV2, Sky 3, even Channel 5. It's wall to wall *Due South* and *Murder She Wrote* from here on in.

Channel hopping last night with a camomile tea I came across the last ten minutes of an Esther Rantzen programme about having a good death. She had been following a man from Powys called Stan as he approached his final days, knowing he was dying of cancer. She asked him in that direct way of hers what he thought a good death was:

'Nice view of the garden. Summer. A gin and tonic. A double. A good book. And cricket on the radio. Then I'd like to just fall asleep.'

It reminded me of what I once described to a friend as my vision of perfect happiness (with whisky instead of gin). I'd bet that most men dream of that kind of uncluttered time. And yet, why shouldn't dying be a moment of peace and tranquillity?

In her last piece to camera with him Rantzen asked what message he'd like to pass on about living to those watching. 'Make the most of what you have. Tell those you love that you love them. That's a good thing to do. Every day. Yes,' he said, without blinking. He died five days later.

Tuesday 4 April

A lot's been happening.

To the Loydells on Friday night for a farewell curry. The sitting room was piled high with boxes. 'Just the CDs, LPs and novels,' said Rupert. 'Haven't even started on the poetry yet.' They were on fine bickering form, like a time-capsule from when we first knew them:

Sue: No, that's Rupert's tikka bhuna, he doesn't do sharing.

Rupert: If I'd have wanted to taste the other ones I would have ordered them!

And:

Sue: No, don't put Rupert's plate in the oven. He likes it cold. He's not normal.

Rupert: So the food can cool down quicker.

Sue: So you can start washing up quicker, you mean.

Luke Kennard, and his fiancé, Zoë, were there. Luke, shy, nervous, eager to please, did a lot of nodding and saying 'Yuh, Yuh,' like he does when he performs his poems. Such a nice, modest man, nothing giving away his hottest-new-talent-on-the-poetry-block status. You know you are getting old when the poets start getting younger . . . and are head, shoulders and torso better than you.

On Saturday to James and Becca Alexander's (40th) Bond party, complete with hired out Casino Royale roulette tables, croupiers etc. Black tie, the works. You pay your £10 each ('to send a cow to Africa'), then play with the 'cashed in' chips. I went as a poor man's Blofeld, in a black polo-neck. Tatty held court on the blackjack table (and did very well), and I found a quiet corner in the roulette scene next to Jasper Hampson, who seemed content to natter about West Brom's fortunes, which look even more disappearing than my own.

Lots of mini-conversations about my villainous appearance, including one with Max Gudgeon, who ended up describing me as 'incredibly brave'. I have never felt this, but thanked him anyway. 'It's not like I have a choice,' I said, by way of an implied reprimand. You can never tell if people hear it or not.

Got a very nice email from Brie Samuels today referring to the time when she 'came out' with MS. She attached a charming but hard-hitting Julia Darling poem about living with cancer. She also said I was brave. I suppose it was 'coming out' in a sense, given that, the school gate aside, it's only the third social occasion we've been to. So I got through a lot of 'How *are* you?' and 'Your head is a lovely shape, you know', without ever really feeling that I could say that I felt pretty shitty to be honest.

On Sunday the most wonderful surprise. Tatty mumbled something about going out 'to get the last bits and pieces for your birthday' while I prepared lunch. She came back half an hour later, and there was Jay hugging me in the kitchen. As if to prove my recent ropey form I immediately began coughing all over him. 'It was either that or crying,' I said, blinking in disbelief. Apparently they fixed it up a whole week ago.

Tatty, flushed with pride at her success, plonked the Sunday papers onto the table and we settled into a companionable, chuckle-filled silence, with coffee. It could have been a scene from Brixton, 1991.

Tatty found not one article but a whole series devoted to the subject of cancer in the *Independent on Sunday*. On pages 6–7 they had made a list of 'vital drugs: what they cost, how they work and who gets them.'

'Look,' she said, *'you're* in here. Rituximab, I mean. But I don't understand it. You've had no problem being treated with it at all. Especially as they describe R-CHOP as the gold standard treatment of NHL. I wonder if they have their facts straight.'

The paper says the following:

- Rituximab costs £15,000 over a five-year period.
- That it is a monoclonal antibody used on lymphatic cancers and in combination with chemotherapy for advanced cases (this made me wince: no one has used the word 'advanced', even if they have the euphemism 'high-grade').
- That it slows the progression of NHL by linking to cancer cells and making them self-destruct.
- That it is approved in Scotland. No NICE (National Institute of Clinical Excellence) decision for England and Wales until next year (again, very odd: no one has described my being treated with Rituximab as 'special', 'unusual' or 'exceptional', nor have they referred to a lack of nationwide approval for its use. I can feel a letter coming on. I'll have to show the paper to Karl to find out how far they got it wrong).

My birthday was perfect, real dark shadows cast by the sun and a beautiful blue for most of the day. By the afternoon it was even warm enough to stride around outside without a hat.

We took Jack and Jena to Michael Caines, having been

treated in the post to a cheque and a card instructing us to do so from Mummy and Daddy. The front of house table in the window, sunlight on our backs. I had carrot and coriander soup, fillet of gurnard and mash, and sticky toffee pudding. An unfussy French Sauvingon, which I had more than a taste of. 'Go on, sir,' the waiter said. 'Finish the bottle. It is your birthday after all.' Jack made me his first ever compilation CD, proudly beaming 'I had to ring PC World to find out how to do it.'

The kids gave me a raclette machine, which we christened for supper, Tatty having brought slices of cheese all weekend from Sainsbury's. There are so many things I never twigged about: the fifth chicken breast defrosting on Sunday morning; the cheese; the pre-washed new potatoes and army of beetroot, gherkins and pickled onion jars lined up in the fridge.

The final surprise she had organised was Paul and Steven coming round after supper for cake and chat. A mellow end to a perfect day. I felt loved from start to finish.

In the midst of all this, still feeling pretty rough. Endless pouring snot and wild coughing fits from nowhere around 3.30 each night. 'You might have mastered going back to sleep, but I haven't,' says Tatty. I now sleep sitting upright from the word go, something I would never have thought possible. Diarrhoea still there, but down to a manageable two episodes a day rather than three. It doesn't sound like a difference, but it is.

Walked into town today to do the car tax. Felt old as I shuffled along in small steps in the bitter wind. Helped Tatty get the lawnmower out and some old tools, then felt guilty for having no energy to help her use them. Came back in and made some v quick decisions about the poems I'll be reading tomorrow at Arvon. Am hugely excited to be going, and it'll be good to catch up on the gos with Andy in the car. However, am still hugely nervous of the wider social event, the meal, the writerly chat, the Q and A. Plus, I'll be full of chemo. Let's hope I don't throw up all over them mid-poem.

This is one of the poems Brie sent:

How To Behave With The Ill

Approach us assertively, try not to
cringe or sidle, it makes us fearful.
Rather walk straight up and smile.
Do not touch us unless invited,
particularly don't squeeze upper arms,
or try to hold our hands, or lower your voice.
Speak evenly. Don't say
How are you? in an underlined voice.
don't say, I heard that you were very ill.
This makes the poorly paranoid.
Be direct, say, 'How's your cancer?'
Try not to say how well they look
compared to when you met in Safeway's.
Please don't cry, or get emotional,
and say how dreadful it all is.
Also (and this is hard I know)
try not to ignore the ill, or to scurry
past, muttering about a bus, the bank.
Remember that this day might be your last
and that it is a miracle that any of us
stands up, breathes, behaves at all.

Julia Darling

Thursday 6 April

A beautiful blue day as Ted Hughes would say. Air warm at
last, with no need for a coat (but I wore one, to be sure). We
went to Jack and Jena's for a sandwich and a bowl of soup.
Admired Jack's new DAB radio/CD player. Discovered something called Radio Chill. Heard at least two tracks I own on
CD. Felt a mixture of cutting edge and middle-aged.

Earlier we sat at the computer and ordered a heap of wooden
garden furniture to replace our rather tired green plastic and
fading Ikea with pine and brown paint. While in retail mode

spent my birthday money on my own DAB portable, a Roberts retro model, in green to match my desk. It will be good for the garden and the cricket once it gets really warm. And this thing called Radio 6, which I've listened to on the telly, now we are digital, and which seems to be directed specifically at people like me, who grew up with Motown then disco then punk then new wave then Echo and the Bunnymen then reggae. Lots to look forward to.

After picking up Shim, Tats had a garden frenzy and we pulled down the ragged and overgrown rose/passion fruit screen on the patio. Discovered a dead Azalea underneath it all. Don't think we've seen it for two years. Decided, while I have energy, to drive to the dump the long way round, having parcelled it all up in a tarpaulin. Traffic appalling, but took Shim and nattered amiably in the sunshine. Job done.

Chemo good yesterday. Was injected by Carol the research nurse, who usually just comes round and ticks lots of side effects boxes (diarrhoea, back pain, vomiting etc.). Was able to clear the Rituximab conundrum with her, from Sunday's paper. What the *IOS* did not make clear is that it isn't offered to low-grade/'indolent' NHL sufferers because, while it is brilliant at reducing tumours by up to 40%, it's not considered cost-effective enough for those tumours which people can have for up to ten years or so. Which makes me feel kind of special really: High-grade, therefore in need of zapping pronto with superdrug, no questions asked. To be fair to the *IOS*, they didn't make the distinction between high- and low-grade very explicit. But then that isn't much of a story.

Before chemo started I shuffled onto the ward and gave one word answers to Gillian the prep-nurse.

'How you feeling, my love?'

'Rough.'

'No better than last time?'

'No.'

'That's a shame.'

'Yes.'

While we waited for the script to come through I learnt that Karl was away. 'Watching Arsenal in Turin?' I said.

'No, on some rock-trip in Cleveland.'

'Oh.'

'Takes all sorts I suppose.'

'It's quieter without him.'

'Nothing we wouldn't say to his face.'

I was introduced to Dr Raj, who asked me lots of questions relating to my cough and cold, and who listened to my chest.

'It's not an infection. Probably most likely a virus which is just taking its time to leave your system. There is no need for further antibiotics. I'm confident that it will clear up soon.'

This raised my spirits enormously.

As I walked into the ward and sat down I very nearly lost it in public for the first time, seriously contemplating leaving the trial and going home. For some reason – I think Tatty reached out and squeezed my hand – I managed to pull back from the brink.

They pronounced my white count 'normal' (14) once more, and the day progressed most pleasantly. Not least because we asked for, and got, a bed, which meant when I conked out, post-Piriton, I really did go to sleep. We got off the bus and met up with Shim just as he crossed the road from school. The world seemed a good place to be.

Came in, plonked down and watched the *Frasier*s Tats had recorded for me on the new digibox. Took the Granisteron (wonder anti-sickness) pill, and, though I looked the colour of wax, felt fine. Shuffled through my poems and waited for Andy to come and collect me. He'd remembered my birthday with a card and a lovely pot of rose petal and greengage jam: 'The best kind of present,' I said. 'You certainly look different', he said.

We drove off and settled almost immediately into a mixture of gossip, banter and work-related ranting.

The drive was stunning, the fields emerging from their winter brown overcoat and the hedges tentatively pushing a green haze. After Hatherleigh Andy said how the oaks along that stretch of road really have the most odd colour at this time of year, not green at all, almost whitish yellow as the first signs of growth come through. Was reminded of that Ted Hughes line in *Season Songs* about an oak tree in December and an oak tree in April looking exactly the same but completely different. At Totleigh – just in the middle of some rather good gossip about two senior British poets – we stopped the car as we went over the top and saw the house for the first time. 'I can never look at this view often enough,' he said. 'Just incredible.' He described to me how one year the flood water from the river, the corner of which we could just see, came right up to the hedge of the next door field from the house. 'It was spooky when you came back in the car. Just this shining flooded valley spread before you.'

The welcome and the vibe at Totleigh were magnificent. Alan Brownjohn, who I had read with at Aldeburgh, in a petrol-green moleskin suit, with shiny mauve tie and matching matt shirt and brown loafers, was all condolence and stooped concern. Ann (Sansom) was warm hugs and stroked hands. Carps one massive bear hug and his customary kiss on the cheek. I recognised a handful of the boys and enquired how many windows they'd broken playing football that week. Ian, sublime in charcoal cardy and linen mandarin shirt, was, for the first time in his life, fagless. He patted his ample tummy. 'Got a personal trainer to take it all off now, haven't I?' he said.

The meal, all four courses of it, would have graced any gastro pub. Evs, the mastermind in the kitchen, surpassed himself. A salad of pear, four cheeses and chick peas; mushroom and wild garlic soup; roast chicken and spuds, with green beans and a cream of tarragon sauce; bread and butter pudding to finish.

Brownjohn sat on my left (I was given head of the table) and Carps on my right. Brownjohn and I reminisced about our reading with Anne Carson. I said to Alan that I spoke three words with her afterwards. 'That's three more than I got,' he sniffed.

He was excellent company for the duration, swapping notes gleefully, though he took some persuading that it was '02, and not '03 or '04. We agreed on the ones we liked best without hesitation, Bill Herbert, Esther Morgan, Katrina Porteous; and on John Hartley Williams's rather scaly performance (despite reading some terrific poems). My main memory is that he insisted on making a huge meal of how his new publisher was far better than his old one, the editor of which was seated only four rows away.

Alan liked the debate as well ('This House Believes Poetry Has Disappeared Up Its Own Arse') with Bill Herbert and Michael Bywater opposing, and Liz Lochhead and John Walsh for, the motion. I remembered it being a thousand times more enjoyable than I though it would be. It included the immortal line of Liz Lochhead's that she would rather read early Heaney and early Muldoon than late Heaney or late Muldoon. Sadly the gifted Radio 4 chair didn't give this insight the airtime it deserved and the argument moved on. 'It's the sort of thing your hear poets say in the pub,' I said. 'But never in articles or publicly. I wish I'd heard more.' Alan nodded sagely.

'Precisely,' he said, eyes glinting with steel.

Later to the snug for Arvon-related horror stories (a senior male poet reading, completely pissed, a whole book of poems from page 1 through to page 83, without a pause, before collapsing an hour and a half later), whisky and banter about music. Nathan's Ipod was playing Dylan in the corner, sparking a debate about what we insist our kids listen to (Hendrix, Stones, Van, The Clash), which turned into a debate about what we would least like them to become 'when they grow up'. 'Conservative' came off worst, closely followed by 'Fundamentalist Christian' and 'Satanist'.

Friday 7 April

Sitting propped up in bed last night writing up yesterday, Shimi crashed in, as he does, enquiring why I was still writing now that I had finished a whole exercise book.

'How many pages was it?' he said.

I looked at the back. '96'.

'So you wrote nearly a hundred pages?'

'Yup.'

'And you still want to do more?'

'Well, I've still got cancer.'

'Is that what you write about?'

'Well, yes.'

'What else?'

'What happens. What people say. Stuff.'

'Why you doing it?'

'So I can remember what it was like. I'm also getting Ellie to type it all up for me. Then I'm going to send it round to try and get it published.'

'That means people will read about me.'

'Yes, it will. But not on every page, don't worry. You're in my poetry anyway already.'

'Yes, but not every poem.'

'No.'

'Why would people want to read about you having cancer?'

'Because that's what people like to read. True stories.'

'You sure?'

A bad-cough night.

Watched a lovely Argentinian movie, *Son of the Bride*, with Tats, about a man whose mother has Alzheimer's. His father, having refused a church wedding because he was a non-believer, decides he wants to take their vows in church, even though they have been together for 44 years, and even though she is ill. This prompts a wholesale rethink of his life, commitment to his girlfriend, his daughter, ex-wife, the whole thing. But it wasn't corny. The set piece scene at the end, where he declares his love through the video screen of his girlfriend's entry-phone at her flat was fantastically acted and had us both in floods. 'I don't want freedom. I want to live by your side forever. Your problems are now my problems.'

Saturday 8 April

Ian, handing me my cheque in the Arvon office, said two things.

One: 'I know you're gonna be all right. I know it.' – to which there is either: 'Thanks, that's kind'; or: 'How do you know? How do you know I'm less mortal than the next man with cancer?' – followed by an argument.

Of course I chose the first.

Two: 'It sounds shit to say this but you're gonna get great material from all of this, you know.'

I've just broken off to watch the Grand National. Watching them pace around with a minute to go I looked at the prices and saw Numbersixvalverde at 11–1 and knew he was my horse. He came in. Stupidly I didn't make it to the internet in time to put a fiver on. A cracking race, three of them jumping together at the last before the elbow.

It made me realise that this really is my favourite time of year, other than early September with its chilly mornings, blazing days. Something about the quick succession of birthday, Boat Race, National, Augusta, Easter, Easter hols, with light suddenly in the garden and buds growing daily on all the trees, even on my shredded fuchsias, fills me with a burgeoning sense of possibility and hope, even as I sit here with cancer, now as much as ever.

Monday 10 April

Two horrendous nights of coughing. Last night the only slight relief the fact that I had videoed Match of the Day 2, so was able to sneak off at the 2.32 visitation of the phlegm-division to watch Chelsea's magisterial 10-man demolition of West Ham. It cheered me enormously. Until Man U/Arsenal came up next, the former a team who look like there is everything to play for still. But seven points is seven points. I am still pinching myself to see that we are top, let alone 'champions-elect'.

To Andy and Amy's yesterday for a superb Sunday lunch with Stella from work: Gammon, roast spuds, leeks, cabbage, purple sprouting, swede and white sauce; followed by chocolate and pear meringue, a recipe from Amy's great Aunt. Everything (except the gammon and the pears) home-grown from the allotment and all delicious. Lovely conversation and a general feeling of being loved: their kids and ours on very good behaviour. A riotous sunny day, warm, like today, sharp shadows.

Had the midway scan this morning. Was in and out pretty quickly. Had to drink a disgusting aniseed-tasting concoction which you mix with water last thing at night and first thing in the morning without eating anything. Was nearly sick as we went past the bakery in the hospital. Actively looked for a corner to throw up in the corridor – the smell of sweet pastries just too much.

On the ironing board as I went through the polo was nearly sick again as they injected me. That warm feeling going down your whole body: I'd forgotten that simultaneous wobble in bowel and gullet. They said that they'd know the result today – tomorrow at least – but that it wouldn't get reported on till later because of a recent backlog. But that if I wanted to ring up by Thursday, that would be fine. 'It being Easter week is another potential hold-up.'

Took the H2 bus back to Magdalen Road and Tats treated me to a fry-up at the café. Was alarmed to note – about two mouthfuls in of my bacon, egg, beans, fried bread, tomato and a sausage – that I couldn't taste any of it. Nor my very large latte. Wolfed the whole thing anyway, then two rounds of toast and marmalade, of which I got just a tingle. Wondered if this is a side effect of the chemo – it can happen; or whether it's one of being bunged up still with a heavy cold; or one from the scan: they do leave an odd metallic taste on the tongue. My tastebuds seem to have recovered during the rest of the day, enough, at least, to sample my avocado on toast (for lunch) and an apple. Shim came in later with chips after swimming with Jason and I certainly tasted those. Not surprisingly, given how much salt they'd shaken on. But a chip is a fine thing, cancer or no.

Wednesday 12 April

The drive yesterday up to Colislinn. We packed up the car in our usual way, a bit chaotically washing and emptying vases, asking Ray to do the bins, raiding the fridge, eventually leaving around midday just as it started to spit with rain. I did the first section up to beyond Birmingham somewhere, Keele, at a guess, then Tatty took over for a glorious run in the lakes, sun out in force, blinding glare from field-puddles and swollen streams. As Tatty drove I realised I'd never really *looked* at the countryside either side of the motorway through Cumbria. The hills, of course, yes; but I mean the lower flatter more rolling bit between Shap and Carlisle. Not as dramatic, but in the beautiful bleak light, with its own majesty.

I didn't let on, but the driving was agony. We stopped about half an hour after Bristol for a latte and a panini. Sitting there waiting for the food to arrive, watching a businessman tuck into a double bacon burger with fries, I felt distinctly woozy and that turning back was the only option. Kept awake by chewing gum and eating all sorts of munchie-goodies bought by Tats at the petrol station. Realised that I only really tasted the cheese and onion crisps: everything else was slightly floury. Had the same experience today at breakfast. Charlotte has brought some Highland heather honey. It barely registered, smell or taste. Ditto her mindblowing Lavazza, which I only got a whiff of when I added sugar to it. So: I still eat like a horse, but increasingly so, little of it seems to make any dent on the taste buds. Is it the chemo or the cold?

Side effects update: lying in the bath yesterday before packing up I noticed my pubes are vanishing. Where there was once a lavish bunch of parsley, there is now a rather bare copse, full of stragglers.

I also noticed my leg hair has gone AWOL. At least, only calf-hair has, on the outside flanks. My muscles now look shaven, like a cyclist's. Lying there I thought I'd try and pull a few chest hairs out to see if they would come easily. I didn't even need to tug.

As we did the section of the A7 after Langholm I had another good look at the hills. Everything sodden and brown and trying to become green again. I realised I hadn't looked at these for years either. Then the awful dawning in my stomach, more of a terror, really, that I wouldn't live to see them again. That the treatment wasn't working and the tumour has not shrunk. A really quiet voice inside saying, *Take your last look*. Awful. I've not had that before, not during chemo, not lying awake at night, not on one of my coughing or diarrhoea trips, that sense of impending death. But I felt it yesterday, strongly, for the first time and it scared the shit out of me. Tats said 'I won't put you under pressure to ring them for the results. It's entirely up to you.' I'm not sure now if I can face it.

Thursday 13 April

A day of pain, and gifts, too. The pain: just that continuing jagging feeling in my side. It had seemed to disappear when treatment commenced, periodically resurfacing for the odd morning or two, but nothing serious. Then, since the end of last week, and especially over the weekend, it's been there, throbbing quietly, a reminder of how the whole thing started. It might of course, be psychosomatic; or a sign that the tumour really is shrinking: it's-hurting-therefore-getting-smaller kind of thing. Which I'm not even sure is logical.

And, post antibiotic-induced diarrhoea, bad constipation, a definite tightening and lack of fluidity.

But Tats says my cold is much less runny and my cough far less noticeable. It's true: no fits to speak of for two nights now, and only a handful of phlegm-hacks each day. Perhaps the virus really is taking its leave.

The gift: a state-of-the-art Sony Walkman MP3 player in the post from Pug and the boys with a 6-Gig capacity. (None of us know how many songs this is, but Bendy and Nell think it's more than 300). Stunning of him to get it so right, and also for organising it so beautifully. He also included a £30 cheque towards 'downloading fun': top man.

Spoke a moment ago to H on the phone and we swapped notes. His story, my story. He has tons of pills to take at home, no injections. 'I'm very lucky,' he kept saying. One of these is Cyclophosphamide (same as me), another is the famous Thalidomide. He forgot the third. His chances, he has been told, 'are more Chelsea than Sunderland.' He's got plasma cytoma, which is a lot better than its fast-spreading cousin, plasma myeloma, so it sounds like they caught it early. 'And I was only going to see the doctors about something else.' Where have I heard that one before?

Have been reading (golly!) a couple of articles in the *Poetry* journal Jean sent me. One, by Tony Hoagland, on 'Fear of Narrative and the Skittery Poem of our Moment', really caught my eye. It will be worth photocopying and sending to Andy, maybe even Rupert, if I can stand the nuclear reaction. He has some lovely lines. He argues that some US poets abjure narrative:

1) because of the emphasis in the 70s and 80s of so much 'confessional' poetry on the 'self', narrowing the range of the form;
2) because our age isn't narrative: i.e. that it is too multi-tracked, visual and fractured to place experience in a 'hierarchical' form in a poem;
3) because of a *fear* of enclosure or submission, of being 'swept away' in the sweep or lyric drive of a poem.

Finally, he says, it is to do with our relationship with knowledge, and, therefore, power, that we are producing poems which risk risking so little, except the ability to play with language. It made me think a lot about my recent stuff. Not that I've written anything since before Christmas, but the stuff I spent ages poring over to go into the new book. I shouldn't really worry. Andy always says the narrative line is absolutely visible and dependable in my work, though I'm never sure if he means this as a compliment. It made me think more specifically that I might try and start a few lines – or that I *should*, anyway. But that response is always dangerous, doing something programmatically, following an idea rather than a cadence or an 'impulse' as Frost put it. I just don't feel them coming at the moment. The only lines I've got stacked up waiting at home are some nervous scribbles about 'Speaking in Tongues' and another about my wart (which seems to have been frightened off by the chemo) *à la* Kenneth Koch. Still, it would be good to do something. I'd like to revisit my 'To my Cousins' and 'To Alcohol' poems from a couple of autumns ago. I'm sure there's material there. That has always been my problem: massive excitement and confidence while I'm on a writing spurt, then withering self-criticism once it is over, leaving pretty much nothing in the drawer. As I've got older the two polar opposites have got worse. The confidence soars like never before (I'm sure because I know it's getting harder, therefore deepening any sense of gratitude), only for the older, wiser head to blue-pencil every other line once the white heat has finished. It is just like manic depression. I know that a time of not writing much straight away after finishing a book is normal, but I'd give anything for lines to start plopping into my head again while I'm up here. Colislinn has always worked for me before.

Earlier – before my nap – spoke to Karl on the ward. My scan hasn't been reported on. He won't see the result till next week, when I see him again on treatment day. So now we know. Nothing. 'But don't worry, Anthony,' he said. 'I'm very confident clinically it's moving in the right direction.'

Good Friday 14 April

The first day without rain, very light and clear, if not massively warm. Jock took Non and I in the Landy – only a Landy could have done it – up a foresty track to the top of Comb Hill, two valleys away, on top of which sits a very windy and rattly radio mast. It reminded me of that Ted Hughes poem 'When Men Got to the Summit'. Massive 360° views, the sort of place where it is only summer, or dry, for a matter of weeks each year. As we rumbled up the track we startled a couple of curlew from their nest on the ground. I'd never seen one before, and was impressed by the curve of their beaks, how black these were, and the size of their wingspan, much bigger than I had imagined. Jock said to me last night after supper as we stood in the living room: 'I know this sounds crass, but I just know you're going to be all right, I just know it.'

To Hawick in the evening for a Stations of the Cross service. The highlight of this was the reading out, at each station, of a rhyming doggerel poem by '12-year-old Nellie', presumably from the church congregation.

It contained deathless lines such as 'Peter had betrayed

Jesus/three times over./What he really needed/was a four leafed clover'; and: 'Jesus was in/a lot of pain./The soldiers they were/really insane.' As Tats said afterwards, the service was too sparsely populated – 30 at most – to run the risk of catching each other's eye and prompting proper church-giggles, though we were all tempted. It reminded me of the time at the church I grew up attending when a lady called Myra would be called upon once a year to 'share her poetic gift' at Easter, say, or Christmas. She always insisted on memorising her verses and often ran into difficulties.

On one occasion she got stuck on a line which went something like 'Oh God, in Heaven above,/we thank you for your power/the evidence of which we see/in the birds, the beasts, the . . .' A pause. I remember very clearly the tension rising in the room, someone coughing with anxiety, then, from near the front row, one of the elders suggesting rhetorically 'the flowers?' It was enough to get the whole row of boys, seated at the back, and by now chewing their hands, to be shown the door, though whether out of crowd control or compassionate concern for hand-injuries was never made clear.

Easter Saturday 15 April

A lovely luminous evening after another mostly sunny and dry day. Shouts from outside, the kids on the trampoline. The boys have been pretty much feral these last two days, hunting in a pack outdoors and only appearing at mealtimes. In fact at lunch they *didn't* appear today, preferring to eat sandwiches in the den, which they have been re-building. They materialised at 6 for hot cross buns, coating each one with half an inch of honey or strawberry jam, shouting, each of their knees a brown rectangle of mud where they have been kneeling to crawl into their cave of winter-fallen branches and moss. It reminded me of the most intense feeing of happiness from about three or four mornings ago. Tats and I had been munching toast quietly and watching the birds on the feeder below the kitchen window – a nuthatch, goldfinches, bullfinches, even a greater spotted woodpecker – when they all burst in in their pyjamas, raiding the shelves for cereal, squawking and beaming. Their aliveness cut me in half, just as an old bit of Abba came on the radio and I named it correctly to shouts of 'saddo!' I live for this kind of serendipitous banter and communal mayhem. I found myself looking away brushing my eyes so they wouldn't see how I was suddenly so close to crying.

Nearly four days now of GCSF (Granocyte/Lengorastin)-related pain, the longest stretch I've enjoyed so far. Sharp-shivery pulses in my Big Bones (femur, pelvis) resulting in lower back ache-grip. Have felt useless both in and out of the house. Tried emptying the dishwasher today and had to have a sit down. Almost constantly breathless. It's laughable, with the amount of food I still love and crave, that I'm mobile at all. Feel beached, bloated and sore.

Have started (re-started, that should be) *Intimations of Mortality* by Violet Weingarten, a journal of a NY novelist's experience of chemotherapy. I like it, but only in small doses. Probably my problem, not hers. But two quotes leapt out at me:

It is time to stop proving things

– this cannot be improved upon, by addition or subtracting and:

I have the present, but not the future. Does anyone? Not really.
But I know it. Except I don't.

– which cannot be improved upon, either.

I have cancer.

I hate it in the pit of my being.

But downstairs *Dr Who* has just started, and I want to be a boy again.

Relapse

Thursday 20 April, Exeter

Yesterday the worst day so far.

Not the chemo, which I am 'sailing through', but the news after it.

After an early finish, say, 2.30, Karl ushered us into consulting room 2, where Felicity Carr sat, and Carol the research nurse on the side. There was a gloomy atmosphere, in spite of Felicity's determined and natural sparkliness.

She began talking before we even sat down. 'It's not good news I'm afraid, the news from the scan. Far from shrinking, your tumour appears to have grown. I can't tell you how disappointed we are.'

She outlined immediately what the next steps will be. I am to leave the R-CHOP regime in favour of E-SHAP, a much more aggressive treatment, which will start on Thursday week. I will have to go in tomorrow, to have a hickman line put in my chest, a device which allows the drugs to be pumped in intravenously, and also at home. I am to have two cycles of this, four weeks apart, and then a bone marrow transplant at the end. They are already talking about getting stem cells from me and about possible donors from my siblings.

Felicity was lovely as ever, but extremely grave underneath it all. She said: 'We are guilty, I suppose, for saying there were such high hopes at the beginning. But 80% are really good odds. I am just so sorry that you, for whatever reason, have fallen into the unlucky 20% for whom it doesn't work. We will of course review everything.' She didn't give me any percentages this time.

I asked her, of course, why they thought it hadn't worked. After a lot of scientific stuff about the Rituximab not really having done its trick and killing the proteins of the tumour, she was left hypothesising, urgently flicking backwards and forwards in my file to the original histology report. I felt a bit gauche to have asked, but I didn't really feel I had a choice.

I then asked ('No, ask away, it's so important') whether they could hypothesise about how long I'd had the disease, as it was the question I'd been asked most by friends. Again, after a lot of scientific stuff about one cell receiving either genetic or radioactive information in order to start growing, she couldn't say. Karl piped in at this point and guessed at around six months, which means it began sometime last summer. I wonder if the virus I fought off at Mart's birthday, when I had hives all over me, was the one which sparked it all off. I was certainly laid low for a couple of weeks after that. In any case, we will never know.

Felicity asked Carol to make us some tea, and after a lot of reiterating the key facts – it will be worse than it has been so far, and will take 4–6 months of further treatment – we got shown into the 'Quiet Room', with its sofas, candles, and soft lighting. We sat in there cuddling for a few minutes before Karl came in again and began chatting about his own cancer. He's had a relapse, he told us, and will be having to drive to Plymouth for radiology. 'My lymph nodes have just gone all over the place,' he said. He looked utterly calm.

'Can I ask you about it?'

'Sure.'

'You've got Hodgkin's, right, which is rarer and less straightforward.'

'Yes. Rarer and my form is certainly less straightforward.'

'How long have you had it?'

'I'm 38 now. I was diagnosed at 16. And I'm still here.'

'Shit.'

'Absolutely. But as I said to you in the ward when you told me you'd been having pain, there's more than one way of skinning a cat.'

'Did you know then?'

'No, but my alarm bells were ringing. It shouldn't be happening. So you taper your language, you know? It's not over yet. You've just got to realise you've been dealt a shit hand of cards and now you've got to play with them.'

'Right.'

'Shit happens,' he said, not losing eye contact.

'That's one of our sayings,' said Tats.

'By the way', she went on. 'This room is a disgusting colour.'

'Good woman,' he said. 'I've always thought it was a pile of crap, from the day they painted it.'

Friday 21 April, 5.45 am

Been awake since four-ish, pre-empting the coughing-strike by nuking it with codeine ('may cause drowsiness, avoid heavy machinery') and then sitting awake (I would say lying awake, but I don't lie down any more) thinking and thinking. At least I didn't wake Tats.

All day yesterday in hospital, mostly having my hickman line put in, or waiting to have it done, then lots of other bits and pieces, like a chest X-ray, oxygen tests etc. In its way, a better day than Wednesday, and, in its way, completely shattering.

We both woke early – yesterday's entry was written in bed before 7 – Tatty around half-four, when she went to the internet and printed off everything to do with E-SHAP and bone marrow transplants, and me not much later, lying blinking in the dark and pretending I could go back to sleep. 'Did you sleep much?' Gillian the nurse said yesterday. 'Not much after four.'

'I don't blame you.' It's amazing how everyone knows, you just see it in their faces. In this sense, and in the way they all banter relentlessly with each other, it is like a family, one where the pain of the few is felt by the many. We even got to meet Felicity Carr's secretary, who presented us with her unerring description, in letter form, to David, Dana and Liv, of my situation: 'I anticipate that Anthony will require treatment for a further 4–6 months.' She was a nice lady, smart steely clothes, very sympathetic. You knew she knew. And she knew that. We didn't make any small talk.

And that was what the whole day was like, really. Brief, intense conversations with everyone, about everything. From the important one with Karl, perched on the side of the bed, about what this all means, to The One About Flushing The Hickman Line, with Gillian giving Tats a hands-on demonstration.

The one with Karl of course lingers longest. It was intended as the one where we'd catch up in real detail all the stuff which flew over our heads on Wednesday. He went back over what would happen. I'm to start E-SHAP on Thursday 4 May (not next Thursday as I'd thought), which means coming in every day afterwards for five consecutive days, all for chemo. Then I go home and use the hickman to pump more drugs. Fourteen days later, just as my white count begins to go up again, they will harvest my stem cells so that when they come to do the transplant they can hopefully use 'me' as the donor. I'm going to repeat this process twice, once in each cycle of E-SHAP, which is all I will get of it. Then in July, when the harvesting is over, and they have hopefully got enough 'good-me' in the can, they can do the transplant, to rebuild marrow from something like scratch. If there isn't enough 'good me' they'll go to Mart, Rich or Sarah.

Only one difficult moment in our time with Karl. Tatty kept herself to dates and technical things like when I'd be in the isolation ward and for how long, but I only had one thing on my mind. Now I was in the 'unlucky' 20% who don't go into remission with R-CHOP, what were the percentages like for E-SHAP? As soon as I heard myself ask the question a) I wished I hadn't and b) I knew he wouldn't be able to tell me. For I think the first time since we've known him he looked uncomfortable and he fudged. I don't blame him, it must easily be the worst part of his job. What he did say – on Tats' prompting that E-SHAP looked like a treatment for the relapse of NHL – was that relapse was effectively where we were, even though we were only a few months away from my first diagnosis. I looked at him and frowned. 'Well,' he said. 'It's like this. Sometimes a relapse is after six months, sometimes a year, sometimes longer. In your case, the R-CHOP probably held the tumour at bay for a little while before it started growing again. So the gap between progress and relapse was in fact very short. If there was one. Ideally we'd usually get you into remission first before E-SHAP, yes, but in your case we don't have a choice.'

'So there aren't any percentages you can give me?'

'Well, there's more left we can do, that's for certain. And it's a big treatment we're embarking on now, that's true. But after, well, then there'd be radiotherapy, if things still weren't going in the right direction.'

'And after?'

'And after, we'd be looking at managing the disease, not cure as such, palliative care.'

'Right.'

'But that's a long way off yet. We're going to give this our best shot.'

Having got up so early I was able to do another 'coming out' email to all and sundry. The replies came thick and fast, from David's 'This is very disheartening news. Rest assured I join with all colleagues at SELL in wishing you the speediest of recoveries' to Jock's 'Make sure you kick this fucker as soon as possible.'

While we were at the hospital Ray, bless him, took delivery of 80 of my new book in a huge spanking cardboard box by special delivery. I picked one out to show Tatty. It looks absolutely lovely, the photo on the front just right, nice blurb and author photo, all very grown-up. Noticed a couple of mistakes – a non-italicised dedication to Andy Brown, a non-centred quote under 'Basil and Chopped Tomatoes' – but nothing most punters will pick up. It's a book, and it has my poems in it, and it is in the world at the same time as I am.

Last night, best bit of the day, one of our four-in-a-bed cuddles with the kids. Lots of fart-banter and giggles and M&S promising evil things to each other without meaning them. A residue of rawness between them, which may take time to heal, having been left for so long unsupervised yesterday. The plan had been for them to be at Robyn and Rory's, but it seems they spent most of it here, latterly at each other's throats. We had to tell them the news.

'Does it mean you'll die?' said Shim, direct as ever.

'No, it means we've got lots more treatment ahead of us which is going to take a long time and which they are very confident will make Dad better,' said Tats.

'It's what they give when the first treatment doesn't really do its stuff,' I said.

'Did they promise you you'd live?' he said.

'No, my love, they can never make promises with cancer.'

'Why not?'

'Because you can only be sure you're not going to get it again once you haven't had it for five years.'

'But Robyn's OK.'

'Yes, but she's been clear for two years now. She's still got a while to go.'

It's the first time I think the potential seriousness of the whole thing has really been laid down with them both in the room at the same time. But if you're going to face your mortality with your kids, doing it in bed, with their head on your chest, while wondering out loud 'who farted?' is the best way I can think of.

Thursday 27 April

I lay awake last night and planned my funeral.

Not in the kind of detail which I can now recall and record, but I definitely had a vision of it, its texture and tone. The only thing I can bring back with any certainty was that I wanted Wes to be in charge of the music – absolutely no organ music whatsoever – by playing pre-made compilations of my favourite tracks as people came in. Perhaps I was really half-asleep and dreamt the whole thing.

The other thing I know I thought about very clearly (though this may have been a dream as well) was that I wanted a cricket match to be played in my memory at Ide – family vs. the Cavaliers – and for my ashes to be scattered in the Slitrig at Colislinn. I have a very clear memory of seeing (dreaming?) Wes and Allie, Simone and Cameron and the kids, Jay and his, Jockie and Charlotte, Nell and Patrick, of course, Claude and Lauren and my family, performing a very simple ceremony, in wellies, in the summer, then having a huge hog roast on the grass with wine and music. I don't know how long I was awake for, but I think it was at the second interruption, some time around half-one, when I went through all this. The odd thing is, I remember the feeling of cool detachment more clearly than I do some of the details. It's the first time I've really gone into that realm, the kind of what-happens-without-me. And in many ways I only just organised or allowed myself to see the first five minutes as it were, not the endless drudgery of February school mornings when they will oversleep and the roast will burn.

On Monday night, a precursor of all this, as Tats and I lay awake talking into the darkness about the possibility that I might die. Again, I don't recall too much of it, more that it was another 'first', where the possibility of travel/summer holidays/money arrangements being changed was faced and discussed tentatively. We assured our love for each other more times than I remember. And I know I said at one point that if I do die the Legal and General life assurance will pay up in full, which is more than they do if I live. It's funny, what you say. You think you'll say something grand and romantic but what you come out with is 'My finances are in about four different folders in the filing cabinet.'

Took Shim to school yesterday and saw Vince and told him the news. Before this he opened with the usual: 'Hi, Ant, you look terrible.' I thanked him for this of course, putting on my best hurt look. He replied: 'I thought you might want it straight, occasionally.' It's funny, all this banter. When you get in a groove with someone and set the tone – sledging at the shops etc. – it's silly to take offence, when you know that's how it's going to be. And yet it really got to me. In some ways he's doing me a favour – I do look terrible, I certainly feel it – by not putting 'How he feels' above the truth, which is what invariably is going on when people say how well I look, i.e. reassuring themselves that things aren't as grim, potentially, as they are.

I should have thanked him.

Still having broken nights. The coughing fits are not as intense as before, that is I don't cough for up to 20 minutes/half an hour and I don't cough as much up, during them, as I used to. Usually I can stagger to the bathroom, take some codeine, and it'll be over in less than five minutes, if that. But the lying half-propped-up, to drain the mucus, is something I'm still not used to. I find myself 'burning up', kicking off the sheets, with no temperature at all, very sweaty. Then half-awake dreams, a sip of water, a bit of clock-watching, then oblivion till the next rasp-tickle shakes my body upright. After our talk in the darkness on Monday I had one of the worst nights ever, feeling, as the *Today* programme came on, that I had not slept for a single second. I suppose I must have, but it felt very much the opposite. The last two mornings I have actually walked Shim to school, hatless now the warmer air is here, for all the world to see what I really am: a small-step-taking well-dressed bald guy who looks short of breath.

8.20 pm: Later

To the hospital this afternoon with Mummy and Daddy (here all week since Tuesday) and Tats to ask Felicity Carr some more questions. Tats drew up a good list two nights ago (at 5 in the morning, obviously).

It begins with asking about the 'investigation' into my relapse. What does that mean and how does it take place? I think Felicity is an enormously skilled doctor and a very gifted human being to boot. She began answering me before I'd even really begun. At this stage it was just Mummy and me with her in the Quiet Room. Daddy was parking the car and Tats hadn't quite got back from school.

We were just getting to the part, having reassured me that it was, indeed, B-cell and not T-cell lymphoma, about the process which histologists go through in making their diagnoses. My histologist would not have reported alone, she said. It was now routine that they went for a second opinion. If there had been any significant doubt, they would have sent the sample to UCL in London, which is the national centre of research excellence on these things. 'He's from UCL anyway, our man, so I was confident they'd got it right.'

At this point, Janette, the specialist nurse, came in and joined us. Ten seconds later she was followed by Tatty and Daddy together, so we went back over the whole thing again for them. Felicity was both humane and thorough throughout, pausing to go over the more arcane scientific jargon, but always full of reassurance that we 'must ask anything you want, anything, that's why we're here.'

Having established who we all were, and a tray of tea having been brought in; and that the enquiry into my results was ongoing as of now, there was a knock on the door. It was Helen, Felicity's secretary. She handed her a piece of paper, about half A4 in size. 'This has just come through, Felicity. It's Anthony's scan report.'

There was a brief silence while Felicity read the words in front of her.

'Well I don't know what to say. It seems that this is saying the opposite of what we believed to be the case last week.'

Another silence.

'The report I have in front of me is saying, Anthony, that your tumour has, in fact, shrunk, as we had hoped.'

'But how come the report last week said exactly the opposite?'

'I really don't know. I'm so sorry to pile on the torture for you like this. It seems it wasn't reported on accurately at all.'

'So the treatment is working after all?'

'Well, according to this, yes.'

At this point Felicity despatched Helen to go and call the radiologist so that they might speak.

As she left, Felicity began to hypothesise about how this may have come about. The multidisciplinary meeting would have taken place, as usual, with many cases to look at. She went on. 'The only thing I can think of to explain it is that, at the end of the meeting, and needing to give a verbal answer to the question of whether your tumour had shrunk or not, he got the slides the wrong way round and looked at the 10th April picture before the 3rd February one, and assumed there'd been an increase in the tumour-mass. That's all I can think of. It sounds to me, if this is correct, in front of me here, that he got them in the wrong order. I am so sorry to have put you through this.'

'But it's the right kind of mistake, if you know what I mean,' said Tatty. 'I'd much rather have it this way round.'

'Well, of course,' said Felicity. 'And it places everything we've said now about your change in treatment in a completely different light.'

'You mean we go back to CHOP-R?' I said.

'Exactly. We keep going with what seems to be working.'

A knock on the door. It was Helen again. 'They've found him and he's on my phone.'

Felicity disappeared, clacking down the corridor. After an endless five minutes of social chit chat with Janette, Felicity appeared in the doorway smiling but saying before she even sat down that we wouldn't have a definite answer till tomorrow. The radiologist was extremely busy now (and upset, she told us) so would have to take the slides home with him. He would call her first thing, after which she would call us. In any event we could always come in again to chat.

After some more blood tests (normal again) and another check of my chest (more antibiotics) I was free to go.

I can't begin to say what a relief this is, nor how nervous I am that it might be another mix up, as if, having mixed it up once, fate will balance things out by sending me back the original result, namely that R-CHOP is not working. We haven't even told the children, we're so wary of getting their hopes up. We told Rich, who came to visit today on the train. But even as we stuck to the wording of the report ('a substantial decrease in the tumour size') Tats refused to get our hopes up saying 'I just can't engage with this emotionally, Richard, at the moment, not until we know for sure.'

Friday 28 April

Felicity phoned at 10 and got to the point straight away, as she always does: 'Anthony, it's Felicity Carr here and it's good news.'

She went on to say that the tumour had shrunk by 90%, going from 4/5 cm in mass (the figure I remember the first ultrasound man quoting to me) to 1/1.5 cm in mass. The treatment is working, and has every chance of continuing to do so. Simple as that.

What is it like, being told you are going to live? You hug your mother, who cries. You phone your wife who goes 'Yipee!' You drink coffee and eat pastries to celebrate. You tell your cleaning ladies, who are so pleased (they *thought* you looked better than last week). You tell your daughter, who is off school with a sore throat. She says 'Why are hospitals so stupid?' You receive many phone calls. But what is it *like*?

It is like watching the light fade from a room, sunlight making patches on the house opposite, the pink tips of apple blossom daring to poke through into the same, as you have done a thousand times before. But this time you know you'll be doing it again, next year, and probably, the year after that.

It is dreaming up something profound to say about Kylie Minogue's post-treatment haircut, and about the newspaper coverage of it, but resisting the urge. Ditto the obituaries you read this week of the man who invented the CT scan and the man who discovered a cure for leukaemia in children. Life is too short, you tell yourself. From now on I will write what I want.

It is darting in and out of the office to check who has sent you the latest congratulatory email.

And remembering that Chelsea only need a point against United at the Bridge tomorrow to win the league.

It is feeling that you might start reading poetry again.

It is breathing in deeply on the doorstep in the sunshine, and, though it induces a coughing fit, being grateful for breath at all.

Life

Bank Holiday Monday 1 May

A sunny day in the garden with Tats. I've managed to contribute at last, by moving a few stones here and there, but the real effort, not least vision, is hers. She's re-positioned many of the raspberries, re-organised the front door border; taken out all the yellow pom-poms (as she calls them); bought tomato bags and planted them up with tomatoes, courgette and cucumber; re-filled and re-planted all the plant pots, pruned the blackberries; and espaliered and re-planted the apricot along the fence with canes. Heroic.

The weekend was alternatively quiet and celebratory. Saturday we phoned round the gang for a barbeque and charged off to Aldi for sausages, chicken, salad etc. Prior to this we made visits to Calor Gas (closed at 12 on a Bank Holiday weekend), Martins the caravan people and B & Q, none of whom had the right kind of canister for us.

Then a sleep. Then everyone turned up at six, even with little kids, for one of those thrown-together evenings which are so much better than the long-term planned ones. We had: chipolatas, butcher's sausages, chicken in lemon, garlic and pesto, Tatty's asparagus wrapped in Parma ham, chicken salad, boiled new potatoes, hot rolls from the oven, followed by strawberries and cream (ice lollies for the littles). Tats pulled out our old self-erecting play tent for the kids and everyone settled into a groove immediately. Present: Paul & Sally, Kari & Steven, Rory & Robyn, Jack & Jena.

I don't remember anything I said to anyone, or anything they said to me, but I do know I wanted it to go on forever, so that I could keep using it to affirm the fact of still living, eating and having friends. Is this what it all comes down to? A few evenings in your garden with your closest, and which you know you will never forget? It was exhausting, but ordinarily, spectacularly, quietly and lovingly an evening of laughter and snatching the moment.

Not only because I'd had a few *Proseccos* and peach juice, I slept the best night's sleep for weeks.

Saturday I sat on the doorstep and chatted to Tats while she re-organised the front door border, digging up fuchsias, moving the baby palm, putting light between the plants. I moved a few stones in the border for her and got completely breathless. Very kindly halfway through Will and Susie from over the road came to share in the good news, with handshakes and smiles. People seem to divide into those who say 'What fantastic news!' and those who say 'I hope you sue the NHS!' Lovely that they are firmly in the former category.

Yesterday at church, Sally stood up and told everyone of her plan for them to pray for me and the family. 'The idea is,' she said, 'that Ant and the family do no work whatsoever, and they feel no pressure to say how much it is or isn't working. So, don't email them to ask what to pray for because that makes more work for them. I leave that to you and God but some ideas are: fun, sleep, laughter, togetherness, hope and faith. And, of course, healing. The other idea isn't that you go into a darkened room for half an hour, but that you stick a post-it note on the coffee jar, or on the buggy or on your shoes, and that when you see the post-it note, you say your prayer for them. On the other post-it note, you just write your idea, so I can collate them all together in a folder. Then they will know what is being prayed for them and at what times. Of course, you leave it anonymous.' I listened to this brushing away tears from my cheeks, trying not to look round at people looking at me. 'We're doing this as the body of God,' she said. 'When one of us hurts, we all hurt. You don't even have to know Ant to commit to praying for him.'

So many memories of Friday. About half an hour after the call with Felicity, Marco Mullen came round to say, in his own words, 'Life's a bitch,' not having heard the news. He stayed for coffee. Halfway through our natter, Maura came in with a card, sobbing. She gave me a hug in the centre of the sitting room, nodded wordlessly at Marco, then left, still sobbing and trying to smile. It was really quite biblical as an act of wordless support and affection; touching, and faintly comic all at once.

My other favourite is Jockie giggling, really giggling, on the phone, just saying over and over 'Those Wilson genes! Those Wilson genes!', as though they had something to do with me getting better.

Tuesday 2 May

Propped up in bed, a lull before Sarah arrives on the train. A cold, grey day, drizzly and a little windy. I knew my new jumper would come in handy. Secretly glad that the plants are all getting watered for free.

Light in spirit but weary in body. Despite the best night for a century – only one coughing fit, to go with my night sweats – woke up feeling as though Daffy Duck had paid another dawn visit. It was all I could do to get downstairs in pyjamas and make Tatty and Bendy a bagel. I'm puzzled – and still a little worried – by my right-side abdomen pain, where the tumour was originally detected. Sometimes it's sharp, jabbing, sometimes a dull ache, the 'sleeping in a draught' ache I described in hospital on January 6th. Mostly it is in the same place, but I've noticed it travelling about, sometimes up, under my ribs, and sometimes approaching the middle of my back. Very weird.

Later

Since the good news, have become aware that events have been occurring in the outside world.

Cancer does do this to you. Suddenly nothing much else matters. The real National Emergency is your Big Bone Pain with the GCSF kicking in, and your breathlessness after the school-walk. How dare the press not cover it? As Violet Weingarten says: 'This is the jerkiest journal of all time. Meanwhile Vietnam falls.' So: good news or not, I'm still infatuated with my own creakiness as I live it each day, the real living reality of feeling crap just about all the time my main song and story. And this leaves me feeling slightly guilty, diminished, somehow, on the news of my improving condition. I should somehow have risen above the chronic kindness, the diarrhoea, the runny nose, the phlegm-producing hack. The thing is, this is what having cancer feels like when you get better, still laden with iatrogenic loveliness, as it always has been.

An example of how the word cancer dominates everything came just the other day.

I was having a coffee in the kitchen and caught the end of a headline about a snooker player from the world championships in Sheffield. What I heard was '. . . was defeated today, leaving him to continue his battle with cancer.'

Two things jumped out at me: the implication in the newsreader's voice that he should never have been at the tournament in the first place, having a far more important 'battle' to engage in; and, second, that it was no real surprise that he had lost because, well, cancer's really serious, isn't it? All of this, just in his tone.

But you know what else is coming. It's that word 'battle' again. It almost had me writing to 5 Live cc. the Director General. I cannot believe that in the twenty-first century we have not yet thought of a better way of describing the fact that someone has a particularly nasty disease. It's the only time we ever use war metaphor where illness is concerned, it seems to me. Why? Could they not have said 'leaving him to continue his treatment for cancer' or 'leaving him to continue with his cancer treatment'? Isn't it more accurate, and, therefore, fairer, not only on the poor snooker player, who has also had a gruelling tournament to play in (of his own free will), but on the rest of us mortals who let our doctors do the battling for us? I suppose that admission is at the heart of it.

What cancer sufferers know – or this one, at least – is that 'battling' the disease is the last thing you feel like doing, especially once chemotherapy starts. So we leave that to the experts, who know what they are doing. Me, I don't want to 'battle' anything. I just want to be made better. Admitting that we – I – don't want to battle runs the risk of looking cowardly and not up for the fight. It also is what really lay behind the 5 Live newsreader's tone, an anxiety that to not call it a 'battle' would be somehow to label the snooker player an ordinary bloke like the rest of us, just someone with ongoing treatment of a particularly nasty kind.

This is what the word cancer does to us. It makes us intensely worried for ourselves. Not just because of all its association with death, but because it attacks our sense of invincibility, and forces us to create a language of needing to do something, in this case fight, in order to outwit it. (Even in a long argument against war metaphor in describing cancer I am ambushed – ha ha! – by my own unwitting use of 'attacks' and 'forces': the best of us go down in the fight . . .)

All of this also applies to the description, yesterday evening, on the same radio station, of a former Liverpool captain's wife having recently 'overcome' the disease.

I applaud her and her husband's work in raising awareness and funds by holding a football match (a repeat of the 1989 cup final classic with Everton), but I object to 'overcoming' the disease, i.e. the media using that phrase, when it is more accurate to say 'has successfully completed her treatment and begun remission.' The unspoken implication, otherwise, is that there is a link between her having a famous (and talented? and fiery? and skilful?) husband and famous (and fit? and talented? and healthy?) footballing friends, and getting better from cancer. Which is tosh. I rejoice in her getting better.

I rejoice in how amazing it feels to know one is going to spend longer living on the planet. But I'm amazed by our inability, in one of the most media-savvy countries on earth, to find a language which is a little less afraid of taking time to describe the process of getting better from cancer as it really is, and not some mock-heroic epic from the medieval ages.

Thursday 4 May

A day of gifts: Rupert sent me the latest Billy Collins book, a 'spare' as he put it. I've just read the first quarter of it in one go, a miracle. I can't think of anyone's poems it is so pleasurable to live within during each poem's duration. It may even get me writing again, an argument he makes in the title poem 'The Trouble with Poetry,' which is that one poem always provokes another. We'll see. I just saw Tats' orchid beginning to wilt in the bedroom and it gave me an idea . . .

So today I am energy-man. Yesterday was chemo, my last day of it before the final two Rituximab-treatments, which finish on the last day of May. I slept through most of it, most likely because they gave me a bed. No sign of Karl, still having treatment in Plymouth. Hugs all round from Carol and Gillian, big smiles and genuine warm relief. A nice moment with Ian who made a gentle forward defensive movement, in reference to our cricket conversation from two weeks ago, saying 'Maybe you'll be doing a bit of this after all . . .' Not much else to report.

Felt done in (as usual) on returning home (couldn't have done a poetry reading, even out loud, propped up in bed . . .) but wasn't sick, though have just noticed that am still burping last night's meals-on-wheels Moussaka, which Tatty kindly said was all mine when she saw a third of it was left at the end. This I will not miss about cancer treatment. (It is 25° today, apparently, the hottest of the year so far. I should be outside under my umbrella, on the new garden furniture, only it hasn't arrived yet . . .)

Duncan, yesterday's doctor, decided against giving me more antibiotics for the cough, as the diarrhoea has been so bad with it. I agreed with him. However, I did spend all of last night in the same bed, no trips to get codeine at half-two, and no ejections to the sofa. Another miracle . . . Let's build on it.

Monday 8 May

Friday seems an aeon ago now – that sun, energy, able to get out – and today is gloomy, cold, damp. The blossom is out now, both lots, crab and apple, former catching up with the latter as always, just a week later. I hope it doesn't rain too strongly and wash it all away.

Later Orla came round with some daffodils, though by then it was too chilly to sit in the garden. I really got caught short with diarrhoea, so left a 'back in five minutes' sticker on the door just in case. Good job I did.

Saturday Shim had Louis over to stay. They played on the computer and Playstation most of the morning while Tatty and I slouched in our PJs and read the paper and drank tea and waited for Merenna to get ready to go into town. They left. Then a fry-up with the boys while listening to my fab new digital radio in the kitchen (from my birthday money). It does indeed have Sports Xtra, which seemed to be hiding when I began playing with it on Friday evening . . . maybe the reception in the kitchen is better . . . my afternoons listening to the cricket are safe.

I think the rest of the day was quite lonely, really. M & T out in town, the boys at the park (till it began raining). Lots of telly in the evening, catching up on recorded episodes of *Without a Trace* and *Murder City*, none of which I felt I watched properly, as I had to go out and rescue Shim from a disco party (!) he'd been invited to. A rubbish night, lots of coughing, followed by a very early wake-up. Not as bad as Friday night, though, where I ended up on the sofa.

Sunday morning crept about downstairs eating 3 breakfasts and reading last week's *Observer* Review till Tats shouted down that she was awake. Came up and over more tea reminisced how when they were little, I would beg the children to be quiet on those early shifts 'so mummy could sleep'. 'The thing is', I told her 'they always ran back to you in the end. Somehow, when I wasn't looking, they'd charge upstairs and jump on you. There I'd be, grasping at their ankles on the stairs shouting "Be quiet or you'll wake mummy!" which of course woke you up.'

'Funny', Tatty said, 'I have no memory of that time at all.'

'And now I have cancer, I'm doing it all over again, still trying to finish the paper, only now I can, because no one else is up.'

Sunday Tats went out. I sat in the garden, with my hat, under an umbrella, and read this week's *Observer*, all about the reshuffle, the new digital radio for company. You can get used to mornings like that. But it was oddly lonely, again. Shim happy on the computer in his last few hours before SATs next week, Merenna out at a kayaking party. I came in and put some vegetables on for roasting for couscous, then spent the rest of the morning shuffling in, then out, unsure if the sun was warm enough or not. The boys vanished to County Hall on their bikes, and, while Tatty went to fetch M from the kayaking party, I did some edging and got breathless. Good to have done it anyway, especially before the rain, which inevitably fell later.

Have felt very strange on this latest round of steroids. Very hot and headachy, with an orange-steroid-man head and face. Also, hungry as a trouper. Marmite on toast a speciality. Lots of fridge-raiding as well. Blocked up all day Saturday then raging diarrhoea last night, to the extent I just lay on the bed, sweating, listening to *Miss Marple* through the door and realising I hadn't washed their uniforms or filled their sock drawers. Not a good end to the weekend. However grown-up you are, you still need clean school uniform on Monday mornings.

Wednesday 10 May

My hair is 'long', according to Tats, which means I'm not shaven-headed any longer, but now have that sparse, light-wispy growth which is the giveaway of the true cancer patient: neither bald nor thinning, it sticks out palely (is it grey or blonde?) looking as though the slightest gust might blow it away for good. I don't really like it. I might gets Tats to take my razor to it one of these days . . .

Still have a raging appetite – for the most odd things, as well. Was making Shim's cream cheese and tomato sandwich for school on Monday and decided I had to have them for lunch as well. Ate half a Danish loaf of lovely fluffy white bread without blinking. Am losing the taste for things I previously munched on/drank like breathing: olives (suddenly too bitter); pesto (makes me feel sick); cheese (ditto); and coffee (just can't face the taste of it at the moment). (Ditto wine, though I let that one go months ago.) The coffee especially is distressing. I was halfway through a bowl yesterday with a nice pain au raisin and it was all I could do not to puke. Is it because of the association with the ward? (I had a pain au raisin during treatment last week.) Quite possibly. I'm still very keen on apples and bananas, though, and marmite. Can you plan for this stuff? You can't, you have to go with it, however counter-intuitive.

The biggest difference between this week and the last is that I've started reading again. That is, holding a book open and getting from one end of the poem/essay to the other. Don't think I'm up to the long haul of fiction yet, but first things first. Have been going back over Carver's last poems (*A New Path To The Waterfall*) and his posthumous *No Heroics, Please*, especially the pieces on his poetry and the short stories and others. There's a lovely line in his introduction to a book of 'best of' North American short stories where he says that a short story should contain what we all *know* but what *no one* is talking about. I like this very much, that kind of 'guilty thing surprised' sort of idea. He makes the whole thing, the hard work of constant revision included, seem doubly important and vital. I should send off my short story off to the Bridport Prize. What on earth do I have to lose?

Before I go . . . just heard the first real sound of summer, a bee knocking, twice, into the window pane, as loud as a finger tap, and, somehow, as hopeful.

Thursday 11 May

A gorgeous May day. Golden and green, as Frank Keating would say. Big Bone Pain and shivers kicked in just after lunch. Slept, and was woken by the phone ringing. How many times has that happened recently? Each time I want to throw it through the window, but answer it dutifully, desperate not to offend whoever-it-is. When I say 'yes' when they ask me if they woke me up I still feel bad that they feel guilty.

So: have been doing what I have been doing all week: dropping off Shim; taking tiny steps home; watching *Frasier*; looking at (and mostly not answering) emails; opening mail; then lying on the bed till lunch, unable (and unwilling) to move; eating a quick sandwich; then falling back onto the bed again – I know I've said it before – completely breathless. Then, around half-two, tiptoe to the shops to get the kids a bun; then collapse for a minute; then go and get Shim and collapse again, pointing him in the direction of said bun in its wrapping while I lie on the bed again. Exactly the same for days now. Aching for it all to end.

Monday 15 May

England making heavy weather of it at Lords. A grey (and briefly sunny) day. Last of the apple blossom clinging to the upper reaches, the crab apple already ragged. As Ted Hughes would say, the beauty contests don't last long. At least the lilac is still out; I give it another week, at the outside.

I haven't begun and finished a night in the same bed for three nights. It goes like this: cough mixture, settle down, sleep for an hour or two, then wake coughing, at only half-midnight or one, say, wake Tatty, who has words, then disappear to the sofa. The funny thing is, once I'm out, I hardly cough at all, sometimes never. This happened last night, which I spent on the big blue sofa by the telly, with only one cushion. Tats suggested when I came back at 6.45 that I only go out for half an hour or so, wait for it to calm down, then come back and rest. I'm not sure. I genuinely think I relax more when I'm elsewhere – why else don't I cough, when lying flat, on only one cushion, my knees around my chest? Very, very odd.

We have recently celebrated Shim's birthday. He opens his presents like Daddy, extremely slowly, taking in each word on every card, fingering them carefully for cheques. We took them (Shim brought Sam) to Harry's for supper. Shim put all four of his green chillies from atop his chilli con carne promptly into his mouth as an act of bravado. He spent the rest of the evening guzzling water, sweating above the lip, and saying he was fine. For pudding we all shared a Harry's Heart Attack. This comes in a six-inch deep, four-inch wide goblet. In layers from the bottom are: chocolate brownies with chocolate sauce; chocolate ice cream; vanilla ice cream; marshmallows. The whole edifice is topped with squirty whipped cream and two flakes at 45° like devil's horns. Sad to say, in spite of Sam's late bid for the dregs, that we were defeated.

I joined them slightly late, having fulfilled my duty to talk at book group about *If Nobody Speaks of Remarkable Things* by Jon McGregor (my choice). I was relieved to find that it went down universally pretty well, with most people saying things like 'it is beautifully written' and 'I haven't read anything like it before.' I did wonder afterwards if people were being generous on account of my illness. Let's agree with him in case he dies.

To Spencer and Maura's, for Spencer's birthday supper, cooked by Spencer in the Sephardic Jewish, i.e. Middle Eastern tradition: potato salad with spring onion and salted lemon; orange segments with cinnamon; roasted peppers; and then for the main course, roasted lamb, and couscous with dates, raisins and almonds. For pudding ('I did this, Spencer doesn't do baking: it's a *male* thing') yoghurt cake, with orange syrup and fruit salad, and pudding wine. As Maura handed out the glasses she made sure Tats and I had the pair which said 'To Have' (mine) and 'To Hold' (hers) 'which is what I feel you've been doing recently.'

We gave her my new book and a 'DJ Ant' compilation. She insisted I read one before supper, so I read 'The Surprise' because I like the ending: 'Your life a garden bench/left out/facing all weathers.'

I sat next to a woman I'd not met before (Lewis and Maura from down the road were there and were sweet and solicitous) called Megan. After hearing (or enduring, most likely) the monologue for a little while she said the usual things like:

'You look incredibly well'
'You're amazingly brave I must say'
'I'm sure you'll be all right'

and then something very brave and insightful which no one has dared say which was: 'Well, sometimes we need a little kick. And maybe this is yours.' She's right, I'm sure of it. If I don't get on after this and finish the novel and short stories I've got planned I really will only have myself to blame.

Tatty's school got the 'brown envelope' call from Ofsted on Friday: they arrive on Wednesday for two days. Hurrah. Tats already glass-eyed and monosyllabic with tiredness (I can hear her on the phone downstairs to a friend from another school, a PE expert, planning a lesson with his advice). Thank God for Kari jumping into the breach with tonight's lasagne and Ben and Jerry's Fossil Fuel (a bit like a Harry's Heart Attack, Shim said) tub of ice cream. They are still giving her Wednesdays off to be in hospital with me, but she will have to charge back straight away afterwards, as soon as I've been Rituximabed. That leaves Thursday for being observed: she's convinced they'll watch her Henry VIII lesson, which she prepped for yesterday by watching David Starkey. The kids have to write an essay arguing whether Catherine of Aragon loved Henry or not. Deep stuff. Listening to her I again had the feeling that I was in the presence of one of those rare teachers you never forget. My A level history was not this alive, nor as interesting.

Big Bone Pain in the morning and now this evening. My thighs are hairless, as are my arms (never very hairy, more downy). I noticed this evening that half my eyebrows seem to be missing, the further away from the centre of my forehead they grow. My fingertips have tingled for nearly a week: not painful, just a warm-electric shock kind of feeling. Bowels: erratic. What the codeine (cough mixture) gives (constipation), the GCSF/antibiotics take away (diarrhoea). Weight: hovering around 13 stone, but not dipping below it, as it threatened to just after Easter. Still having that lower back pain which kicked this whole thing off. Am prepared to ignore it. For now. But I do want answers. Fingernails: curving, some with valleys in them.

I lay on Shim's bed with him the other night, after his story, talking to the ceiling.
    'How long have you been ill, dad?'
    'Don't know. They think since last summer.'
    A pause.
    'Almost a year?'
    'How do you get it?'
    'They don't really know. They think that the lymph nodes fight off another illness and that for some reason, one cell in the lymph nodes starts growing. Like it receives a bit of energy, perhaps from radiation, or genetically – they don't know – then it starts splitting and growing and growing, and soon it's a tumour.'

'Is it just bad luck then?'
'Yes. Just really bad luck.'
'Is there anything you can do not to get it?'
'Not really.'
'But you are getting better?'

Tuesday 16 May

England drew in the end. Just couldn't bowl Sri Lanka out. I listened to the whole thing on my fab Roberts Radio, in a mixture of rapture and apoplexy. Lovely sound, very warm. Some great howlers: Blowers calling Monty Panesar Monty Python; then Lord's the Oval. It must have been Alec Stewart putting him off. I love his one word sentences. 'And. There. Is. No. Run.'; 'My. Dear. Old. Thing.'

Fred Trueman, the greatest English fast bowler etc. etc., has cancer, according to *Test Match Special*. As soon as they announced it, solemnly, by Christopher Martin Jenkins, I began laying bets with myself about how long it would be before they said '. . . but if anyone can fight this, Fred can.' It took just two seconds. I timed it. And they used those exact words. (It wasn't clear whether CMJ was reading a Yorkshire CC press statement, or merely voicing his own opinion.) A friend who has myeloma reported people saying exactly the same thing to him. Why do we insist on the language of fight when talking about cancer? Is it that we resort to it in Fred's instance because he was a fast bowler of incomparable fieryness? Or that to *not* say 'he will fight it' is somehow to question his moral/physical strength/courage, thereby letting him down? Again, I nearly wrote in. But no.

Thursday 18 May

8.30 pm

Day after my penultimate treatment.

What a difference not having chemotherapy makes. Yesterday it was just – just! – Rituximab, a nice Piriton and Paracetamol chaser to take the edge off, and away I went, stretched out on a bed with my Walkman in la-la land.

Duncan decided to put me back on antibiotics, as he heard something in my chest. This time it's a double whammy of Augmentin (horse pills, three times a day) and Doxycycline (once a day). Duncan says that if it isn't clearing up by next time (two weeks away), they might get me looked at by a sinus man. 'It's basically like a puddle in there,' he said. 'It has nowhere to run off to as it's a self-contained system. But first things first, eh?' Which is as pithy a summary of the whole cough/snot saga, and their view of it on the scale of importance, as anything I've heard from anyone.

A feeling of total joy – I actually punched the air – this morning lying in bed and waking next to Tatty. When was the last time I did this? Like a normal chemo night (I suppose not, when you think that I suddenly had no steroids zinging round my system) I lay awake and so crawled off to watch the *Frasier* I'd recorded (The One Where They Go To Car Maintenance Class), came back, headed off a coughing attack with some codeine, then, er, slept. And that was it. Next thing I know, Tatty was shouting 'well done, you did it.'

Some new terminology from yesterday. The 'ripples' on my fingernails – horizontal grooves or miniature valleys – which appear weeks after each chemo treatment, are called 'beau' lines. No one knows why.

'That'll be something to take to your dinner party,' said Gillian.

I'm still amazed by Tatty's forbearance of these days at the chemo-face. Apart from the fact that all the attention is on me and that there's loads of ill people attached to drips and bags of blood (I noticed a very thin – and quiet – Geraldine in the far corner of the ward, a shadow of what she was even a month ago, and she looked rubbish then) it must be so dull knowing that within ten minutes of the Piriton kicking in that I'll nod off and remain that way for 2–3 hours. The big difference yesterday was Ofsted paperwork. Very kind of the school to let her come at all. The results are in: they dropped points on only one 'cell' (assessment, I think) and were otherwise fine. The unofficial line is that for a school 'with "notice to improve" (Stalinist jargon) they've done well; are, in fact, "an improving school."' So while they're getting better, observably, they're now also being *told* that they need to get better still just in case they think they've improved enough and can start coasting.

More hospital dates. Final CT on June 6th. If it's a good one (i.e. even more reduction of the tumour) then I'll have a PET scan late on in the holidays, possibly September. If it isn't so good (i.e. there's the possibility that it may still be alive, or that it hasn't shrunk enough) they'll send me up for the PET quite quickly, to make double sure. It's never over till it's over.

Meanwhile, I'm booked in for my 'rainy day' stem cell harvest (just in case) at the beginning of July, for four days, 3, 4, 5 and 6, which will mean taking Granocyte/GCSF injections for a day or two beforehand, to boost the white cell count once more. A general air, in all these conversations, that I am moving towards the end, but that no one is counting their chickens.

As Jay put it on the phone today: 'The light at the end of the tunnel might not be an oncoming train.'

Sunday 21 May

Morning

Sitting propped up in bed with Tats, a breakfast tray at my feet, while she does the crossword in *The Week*. Bliss. Outside the rain it raineth.

Last night we watched the Eurovision song contest (the UK came 19th) with the kids. We scored each act, shouted at the telly, laughed, the whole shooting match. The act I ironically used my '*dix points*' for – Finland: six figures in orc-gear, invisible behind their toothy masks – won the thing by a street. The song was called 'Hard Rock Hallelujah' and was really a case of so-bad-it-was-good.

Wogan's commentary on the whole thing is still one of the broadcast marvels of the year. He takes you through the voting in particular with the driest of injections. 'Here come the Ukraine votes. Let's see if they have anything to spare for non-neighbours.'

Wednesday 24 May

A rare visit to the kitchen to do some writing. And that's the odd thing. In spirit I'm feeling good, that the mojo is coming back, as Tatty puts it. And perhaps she is right: last night I cooked the family meal – garlic and pesto chicken, with lemon and cayenne pepper; roast new potatoes with rosemary; asparagus wrapped in parma ham ('Two nights in a row', Shimi pronounced) – while listening to a funk CD. Could you have a more emblematic picture of good spirits?

And yet: there's a dreadful nagging ache constantly in my knees (I wonder if it's from all those cough-episodes, curled up on the sofa), and a feeling that my calves are now made of water. So: I can keep up with Shimi on the school-walk, am not breathless when I return, but still need to lie down when I do because I hurt everywhere. It's as though my mind is already back on the bike while the rest of me still needs to sleep for two hours in the afternoon. Maybe I should listen.

I've noticed I'm able and want to drink coffee again. Only a cup a day, mind, but it's surely something. No pesto-reaction last night either: I deliberately put in quite a lot of cayenne to see if I'd get that burning reflux up and down my gullet, but nothing. All good signs. Next I'd like to aim for a nice cheese sandwich (or on toast), but have a feeling that this could still be a couple of weeks away, so synonymous is it with hospital eating (it's what I took with me on the first treatment), and, therefore, feeling sick.

An interesting thing re the fatigue. Tats said that even in the last stages the chemo, when I was at my lowest ebb, Carol only ever scored me as a 2 out of 4. (I never see what she writes as I answer her questions.) I asked her what a 4 stood for. 'Totally incapacitated,' she said. It's all relative. For Anthony Wilson, previously fit and healthy, that's what it's felt like. For a seventy-two-year-old living on his own or with his dog in Crediton it's going to be a very different story. You've got to be thankful.

Another interesting fact, which Duncan talked me through: blood-splinters in your fingernails. You get them as signs of the body having had an infection. The blood vessels being at their smallest at the end of the line – the fingertips – they 'explode' or 'leak' into the fingernail, appearing as splinters: little dark streaks of blood below the surface of the nail. If you have six or more at any one time, it's something to worry about. Duncan counted four on me (though today, one week later, I can only count three). 'It'll be your chest, and, possibly, your sinuses, that's what it'll be,' he said. 'Though, as I've said, if we can't knock the cough on the head this time, we'll just have to wait for your immune system to catch up. Ditto the sinuses.' The cough, for the record, has been very well-behaved. A tiny episode last night at about 1.50, but the codeine dealt with it. Otherwise, of late I've had six out of seven nights waking up in my own bed. Miracles can happen.

Thursday 25 May

Sitting up in bed, Sri Lanka 69 for 6. First sun after days of rain. Henry Blofeld has just described Hoggard running in as being 'like a man trying to push himself through a wall', and Monty Panesar chasing a ball at cover as having 'rather a prancing run, like a horse doing dressage.'

This morning I watched *Frasier*, as usual, (The One Where Ros Sacks Frasier From Doing The Voiceover On Her Space

Documentary) then David Attenborough from last night on global warming, then a recording of *The History Man*. The Attenborough was, like *Planet Earth* before it, urgent and elegiac towards both its subject and its medium. At one point, in a sequence where we see him being driven round London in a black cab, he voices his concern for his own contribution to global warming, 'having travelled all over the world to make the films I did.' Not many presenters voice their guilt publicly in this way.

The programme ended with Attenborough talking to a prof from the Met Office (Dilshan has just gone, caught at first slip by Trescothick, moments after Gus Fraser had set them the target of 200) and creating a graph of global warming on the floor of the Turbine Hall of Tate Modern. This did not seem to be overstating the case.

Friday 26 May

Can you ever say final? Is this ever over? I realise both my desire for it to be so, and my terror at the prospect, at being defined not by being ill any more, but by being, well, me, my 'normal' self, pre-disease, Anthony, who cycled to work, stayed up late and liked a glass of wine. Is that who I am? I had my first glass of red this week (with Pug), and, tonight, my first glass of white. If I stay up late, it's because I'm being kept awake by coughing. And I can't even get up the stairs without a sit down. But is that who I am? And if I go back, say, tomorrow, to my 'fit', able-to-drink-and-stay-up-self, is that who I am any more? I realised today, as I muttered inwardly at some minor impatience with the children, that I am very likely to go back to being just as selfish – and lazy – as before. Having had acres of time to waste, in which all I've done is do the school-walk, watch *Frasier*, rest, make a sandwich, rest, buy a bun for the children and do the school-walk again, I'm now terrified at the thought of having it taken away from me, especially by the idea of work – not writing, I mean *work*. And I can project into the future enough to see myself reacting as I always have under pressure to do the things I've really always wanted to do but never really done, write novels and short stories and plays, which is to procrastinate while inventing excuses about papers which need writing, etc. The thought that I am going to get better and have to face the moment when I'll have to get on and do it, for better or worse, really scares me. Not as much as dying. Or having a relapse. In that context, you'd think I'd have no choice but to bloody well get on with it. But I do know myself; and I know I can lie to myself pretty effectively, outwitting that ability – and desire – to lie, not using 'being tired' as an excuse not to write is, after getting well, the main challenge from here on in. I will only have myself to blame.

Sunday 28 May

A very poetry nightmare last night. I dreamed I was reading the new book out loud to Michael Laskey and Naomi Jaffa, with various family members walking in and out while I did so. So far so scary. But the thing was, as I got to the end of each poem, more words kept appearing at the end of the page, like re-drafting in reverse: instead of taking words away, honing the poem, they got more verbose. This happened to 'People in the Life' in particular, I remember. It was like wading through fast-setting concrete, a feeling of utter panic and defeat. The look in Laskey's eyes was a mixture of compassion, and concern that I'd clearly lost my touch. He was too polite to say anything afterwards, which isn't really like him.

When I woke – after the immediate feeling of relief that 'It was only a dream' – I realised that this is a variation on my recurring dream/nightmare scenario. It usually follows this story: I am about to give a reading/lecture/talk somewhere, and arrive to find I have left said lecture/talk/reading at home. Or, I'm on my way to the event, and suddenly I'm three hours late for it. Or, I turn up on time, with the briefcase actually full of notes/books, but no one is there to hear me. Or, I'm doing O level history or A level English, and as I write, the words erase themselves on the page in front of me. Or I suddenly know nothing about *Othello* during the same, not even the name of his trusty lieutenant, doesn't his name start with an 'I'? Poems actually extending themselves, and becoming unreadable in process, is a new one to me. I wonder which variation I'll be subjected to next.

Wednesday 31 May

My last day of treatment.

A bright sunny day, much warmer than of late.

The day began comically, with me meeting Rory in the street and asking how Shimi was. 'Yup, happy to see him later,' he said.

'He's in your house right now.' I said. 'He was over for a sleepover last night.'

'Oh, was he?'

'Yes, with Sam.'

'Oh, OK then. Right.'

As we knocked on Dawn's door for our lift I handed the fiver I'd promised Shim, for his lunch, over to Rory, through his door.

'He's not actually here, Ant.'

'What?'

'Well, it's just Sam in his room. I've just checked.' Cue general panic, laughter from Dawn, and Tatty striding back to the house to check Shim's bedroom.

By the time she got back Rory was in the doorway again.

'Sorry. Got it wrong. He was there after all. Fast asleep. Under some covers.'

Gillian wondered why we were so late, so we had to tell her.

'It's half term, so they're out at friends', we began nervously.

She lost no time afterwards telling me that the 'bum-fluff hair will have to go. It comes back much quicker if you shave it,' and that I looked 'not nearly as bad as a few weeks ago, loads more colour you've got.' This wasn't as bad as Felicity Carr waking me up from my Piriton-snooze later on with the words 'You're still a bit pasty aren't you?'

It was nice to see her. I'm seeing her next on the 13th, one week after my scan. 'This time we'll get it written properly, not reported on quickly,' she beamed.

'Depending on what it says, we can then hopefully take your hickman line out,' she said.

It will affect everything, not just the summer and the hickman line. If it's shrunk to vanishing point, then my treatment is over, bar a final check-up PET scan in London. If it hasn't, I could be due even more. I can't think about it.

Friday 2 June

A warm day. Shim did the lawn for a fiver ('Can you pay me now, please?') and I managed to edge one half before exhaustion set in. The stand-in research nurse on Wednesday said I can expect energy to return 'not before 6–8 weeks, really.' That's fine. It's better to know. She also said that aching joints are normal for this stage of the proceedings, ditto muscles. Which explains the knee-pain, quite different from the Big Bone Pain of the GCSF days. Diarrhoea a presence, but easing off today, perhaps for good (?). Everyone delighted with my improved, that is, absent, cough. Finally learned from Duncan (Karl is still off 'hunting rocks in the sun', but Gillian's demeanour suggested he still wasn't well) why they give you steroids. 'They're anti-inflammatory. Basically, we give them to you as part of the chemo. If we gave you nothing else they would work for a while, in other words shrink the tumour. But it would always come back. It needs to be given in combination, ideally, for it to work for good.' Something Karl said to me in February returned, about very old patients just being given steroids, and nothing else. I'm guessing that this would be very much a holding treatment, but Duncan didn't really go into this. It's funny, now I'm almost done, I actually find I've got a mind to concentrate on what's been done to me.

Sunday 4 June

Yesterday evening we all piled into the Bongo and went off to Budleigh with Robyn and Rory for fish and chips.

We sat on the shingle and watched the mackerel-anglers chasing suddenly materialising shoals, which appeared just under the surface as though an invisible child had just flung a handful of pebbles into the flat water. We queued for nearly an hour for our food. The fish was hot, in batter that was both crunchy and melting. We ate with our fingers and lobbed stones at the point where the waves met the shore hoping for a satisfactory plop. We drank lemonade and ginger beer from the can, brands which none of us had heard of.

Later, I quizzed Robyn about her treatment, as the children sloped off towards the cliffs.

'Robyn, did your fingernails go all wrinkly like mine have?'

'Completely,' she said. 'You could spot each treatment pulsing through, like a wave.'

'And how often do you get checked up on?'

'Every six months at the moment, but soon it'll be a year. The thing is,' she faltered at this point, tears beginning to prick her eyes, 'It actually gets worse the further you move away from it. I'm two years clear at the moment, but nearly the whole time I'm thinking 'What happens if it comes back?''

This had the effect of shutting me up, at least momentarily. Then we pondered together, the four of us, the outcome of my scan on Tuesday, and the prospect of recovering in warmer weather, and about returning to work: 'Don't do it until you're absolutely ready. You won't feel normal again until October anyway,' Robyn said.

Monday 5 June

Other little signs of 'getting better.' Tatty reached over for a snog last night and as rapidly called a halt to proceedings claiming she'd got a rash from the stubble on my chin. 'You've got hair!' she exclaimed. 'When was the last time you shaved?'

'Three days ago?' I said.

'Well, it's growing! And don't tell me, I know what's coming next.'

'What?'

'That it's not all that's growing,' she said, pretending to be me sounding dirty.

While I've been ill the fridge-magnet-poetry-fairies have been at work. Some of it wouldn't look out of place in the more experimental poetry journals:

    the frantic rainy sky is
    always swimming above her head

There's also great nonsense to be had:

    top love is played by my blue cooking rock
    and lusts for white forest milk like dresses chanting
    winter moans

Which I think has a certain lyrical grace underneath the madness. Who is the author/culprit?

    please wax me

reads one contribution towards the lower part of the door, and, just above it

    lick hot delirious hair in summer.

The giveaway, one of the first lines to burst onto this scene reads:

for a moment I could
watch the enormous pink
breasts

Was it John Ashbery sneaking in one night, or the ghost of Kenneth Koch? I think it was Shimi announcing the beginning of his puberty, aged 11, possibly with the help of friends as they raided the cupboard for chocolate milk.

Tuesday 6 June

Scan day.

Am sitting in the kitchen with coffee having had an early lunch. Am not allowed to eat from 12 onwards (8 minutes' time). Have taken the same disgusting drink as last time, Gastrografin. It's very aniseedy; you need a good go of mouthwash afterwards. In my scan-letter it said they're going to do the following:

CT of the thorax with contrast enhancement
CT of the abdomen with contrast enhancement
CT of the pelvis with contrast enhancement

This is two more (pelvis and thorax) than last time. It must be a) to check the tumour has shrunk/disappeared and b) to double check it hasn't spread anywhere else.

I do hate lying there and feeling the hot knife of the liquid surge through my body, plus the simultaneous feeling of being about to throw up and shit myself. The clipped ghostly tones of the voice inside the polo ('Hold your breath please' – pause – 'Breathe away normally') are fully sci-fi, as though from a story by a child imagining 'Doctors in the Future'.

I've taken the required 400 mls of water-mixed-with-Gastrografin, and can report that the final mouthful nearly made me throw up. I had to run (not easy) up to the bathroom to get to the mouthwash. Close. They say in the letter that it's a procedure which doesn't hurt and has no side effects. True, but I feel this doesn't cover it. The boredom of waiting, the talking about nothing to your spouse, the sitting with other bald patients in their gowns in the corridor, the boredom of waiting. On one occasion an old woman sitting opposite me in the waiting room nearly revealed all, by accident, as she bent over to pick up her shoes. She hadn't done her gown up at the back, so the thing fell down over her shoulders. Had her friend not reacted so swiftly we could have all been in trouble. The thing was, I remember the look of utter indifference in her eyes, as though to say 'I've suffered so many indignities already, what difference will it make if you all see my breasts?'

More rage today about cancer-language. I was channel hopping after *Frasier* and caught Lorraine Kelly interviewing a 24-year-old woman about her breast cancer. (It turns out she is the subject of a documentary tonight on ITV, one of those fly-on-the-wall films which follow you for a year.) In the clip I saw she discovers from her consultant that she does, indeed, have the 'rogue' gene that many other women in her family carry and the (male) consultant touching her arm and asking if she is all right. Despite being the news she has expected, it is clearly traumatic: she has already decided that if she carries the gene she will have a double mastectomy.

My problem is with none of these people; it is with the programme makers. As we see the woman walking down the corridor to the consulting room (with her mother, who has also had a double mastectomy) the voiceover intones: 'This will be the moment where Becci discovers whether she has the gene lying in wait for her.' It's the 'lying in wait' I can't stand.

Only cancer makes us react in this way. We don't talk of the common cold 'lying in wait' for people, or sore backs, or a sprained ankle. So why cancer? Of course, it's because we're terrified of it, though, ironically, closer to a cure for it than we are able an 'invisible' enemy force, almost as if we are talking about guerrilla warfare or Iraqi insurgents. We can't defeat it or understand it, so it follows it has to be demonised.

Cancer-books are no better. For the first time since my diagnosis I went on Amazon yesterday and browsed book titles on the subject. I noticed two things: first, that the market is overwhelmingly geared towards women (the subject of breast cancer is by far the most common); and second, that it appears to be the duty of the reader to 'beat' the cancer themselves. (The word 'beat' is not made up: it comes from a book called *Eat to Beat Cancer: A Nutritional Guide with 40 Delicious Recipes*.)

I'm not too surprised by the feminine angle of much of this literature. While I did find one or two books on prostate cancer, it simply appears that women are either better at talking about cancer than men, or perhaps that they just want to talk about it more than we do. This might be borne out by the fact that, the afterword in Ruth Picardie's book notwithstanding, I have found only one cancer-memoir (so far) by a man, John Diamond's *C*.

I don't really blame the publishers of books with titles like *Beating Cancer with Nutrition: Optimal Nutrition Can Improve the Outcome in Medically-Treated Cancer Patients*: we all have to pay the mortgage. But I detest the war language in the above and in titles like *The Plant Programme: Recipes for Fighting Breast and Prostate Cancer*. As if the poor patient reading these hasn't enough on their plate already (sorry). Not only do they have to 'be strong' and 'fight' the disease they suddenly have to become top-drawer cooks sourcing purely organic produce.

In the Top 30 of Amazon's cancer books I counted, in the titles alone, two uses of 'overcoming', three of 'beat'/'beating', the same for 'fight'/'fighting', and one each for 'struggle', 'tackle', 'arsenal' (as in 'the natural arsenal of disease-fighting tools' – yum), 'challenge' and, finally, 'outsmart'. What are we doing here? Outwitting Al-Qaeda? Scaling the south-west face of Everest? No, we are being treated for cancer. The most sane-sounding book I found was simply called

What to Eat if You Have Cancer: A Guide to Nutritional Therapy, not a struggle or a fight in sight. I nearly went on 1-click just to register my approval.

By far the most common word used in the top 30 titles, however, was 'prevent'/'prevention', often in conjunction with the word 'plan', as in 'prevention plan'. To my mind, if you have shelled out £14.25 for *Everything You Need to Know to Help You Beat Cancer: The Ultimate Guide for People Who Have Cancer and Everyone Who Wants to Prevent it*, you either a) already have cancer and want some help with understanding it b) are convinced you are going to get it anyway and are actively looking for signs of it or c) fully subscribe to the idea that it's your responsibility to be cured of it and are secretly ashamed you contracted it in the first place. The thing is I'll bet most people who get cancer aren't really looking for it and don't know what the signs are. And while this book is probably extremely useful (why the 'ultimate' guide? Why not just 'a guide?') in detailing symptoms and signs, it has a nasty whiff of judgementalism about it. Who wouldn't want to prevent cancer? It's almost as if the book is daring you not to buy it.

And yet, I haven't, and won't, and nor will millions of other people, some of whom will get cancer and some of whom won't. Does this make us worse human beings? Such book titles imply that it does, which, taken to a logical extreme, almost implies that we deserve it and that we only have ourselves to blame if we don't recover. I'd rather read *Chemotherapy and Radiation for Dummies* (I'm not making this up): it feels more honest.

Wednesday 7 June

After the scan yesterday we raided the kitchen: toast and tea (Tatty) and cold boiled potatoes and hollandaise sauce (me). My hunger-cravings are one of the more unpredictable aspects of this whole business. And yet if you asked me was nausea one of the main side effects of chemotherapy I'd say no. What chemotherapy *has* done, most certainly, is change the way I *sense* food, that is, remember its taste, texture and smell and the way I desire it in the same ways.

Most acute of these experiences has been smell. Coffee. I couldn't bear the smell for weeks. Bizarrely, bacon of all things would also have me leaving the room (I cooked some for Bendy and Ellie for supper last week, and it was fine.) The worst smell of all, however, was that 'freshly baked bread' aroma which supermarkets and sandwich shops seem to pump out at will. Once, I nearly gagged in the foyer of the hospital opposite their bakery; and last week on a first-thing-in-the-morning trip to Spar for milk I was practically out of the door before I'd even walked in. I think in both cases it's more that they're heating up pastry (i.e. not just bread) that's been pre-cooked which gets me. It's sickly, slightly sweet and *heavy*: for some reason I can't help associating it with cold-ache injections in my arm and moving stiffly down corridors.

Later

Some things I will admit to:

> feeling a mixture of anxiety and anger going to church
> and answering everyone's questions
> every week
> especially when they say things like
> 'You look like you've got some colour
> back into your cheeks, not like last week
> when you looked so grey'
> and remembering what they said then
> and it was
> 'You look *really well*'
>
> feeling nervous at the school gate
> and wishing every day was sunny
> so you could cover up in baseball cap
> and sunglasses
> and avoid eye contact

the loveliness of the days
now I'm more conscious
i.e. not in bed all the time
and the visitors have dried up

the merest hint of irritation
watching *Frasier*
the last two mornings
the unthinkable thought
that it might not be as hilarious as you thought

the almost permanent feeling
of horniness

the guilt
at not having done bedtimes
with the children properly for four months
the wave of inertia that hits you
now you have resolved
to begin doing stories and praying again

the guilt of this
as you watch another recorded episode
of *Without a Trace*

Sunday 11 June

To Guy and Jemima's party last night. It was one of those extremely rare occasions where you sit in someone's garden and feel warm the whole time. Also, that everyone you wanted to see turned up, plus that you could hear them talk.

Tats and I made a bit of an encampment on some chairs on a little patio halfway down Guy and Jemima's garden with Vic and Tamsin, Becca, and variously, Adam Olsen, Jasper Hampson and Marco and Juliette.

Some people were there who we hadn't seen for months, or only in passing at Becca and James Alexander's Bond-do.

Rarely, it was also a party where you actually talk about stuff, in other words not just schools and house prices. (I wonder if, having gone through all of this, I will ever want to again.)

Later, once we'd put our jumpers on and Guy had lit the lamps, Jasper Hampson asked me if the experience of having cancer had changed what I thought about God. I was suddenly aware of everyone hanging on my every word. 'Well, it hasn't made me angry,' I said, to his raised eyebrows. Then I heard myself say: 'I made a decision really early on not to go down the avenue of asking "why me?" Partly this is because you never get an answer – there isn't one, is there? – and partly because you can quickly get lost in a vortex of self-pity, and go mad, basically.' I blinked at him. 'So I suppose I was being pragmatic, really.'

I could feel myself warming to my theme. 'There is one thing: I find that when I pray – if I do – my prayers are much more simple than before, like a child's. Much more "Help me! Help me!" or "Thank you! Thank you!" than anything else, as if the clutter has been cleared away.'

'We're here to learn from you,' Tamsin said then. So I said: 'OK, the things which have irritated me most are people saying "I know you'll be fine" and "You've got to stay positive/be strong/fight it." Becca was quickest off the mark here. "Exactly," she said. "How dare they play God with you?" They don't know. None of us does. And as for "being strong", well that's just bollocks. Being strong is, I imagine, the last thing you feel like.'

Here is another thing I have learned: there are three types of people in the world: the kind who say 'I'll ring you and come and visit', then don't; the kind who say 'I'll ring you and come and visit,' then do; the kind who make no promises at all, but still ring and come and visit. I know which category every single one of my friends and colleagues belong to.

I have three eyelashes left on each eye.

Monday 12 June

Bendy off school again, making sure she gets back to 100%.

I woke today with a feeling I haven't had since – ooh – December: a hangover. The slightest of self-inflicted wounds, it was, unmistakably, a little bit of a throbber. Two-and-a-half glasses but it undoubtedly made me think two things: maybe I am getting better after all; and, conversely, perhaps I should cut back a little – if my body is sending me the signal that it is not ready yet to resume normal Sunday evening behaviour.

Perversely, the irritation of the headache aside, it gave me the most odd feeling of euphoria. It was as though I'd had a brief taste of just being well, *well* again.

My song of the year? k.d. lang's version of 'A Case of You'. A song of communion and possession, release and letting go, I suddenly had the feeling, listening to it the other day, that it was actually a hymn to chemotherapy. In terms of treatment I have had more than the case of wine the song specifies, but here I am, still on my feet: it finished me off, bent double over the sink in the kitchen, turtle doves flitting in the garden, everything flushed with life.

Results

Tuesday 13 June

Scan results day.

Woke convinced that the cancer has spread to my bones. Have persuaded myself that the return of the pain in my side is not psychosomatic, the obvious explanation, but proof of the true virulence of my disease. Sat in the bath and felt very glum. In half an hour Tats will be here to pick me up. Have been useless all morning, not able to concentrate on a thing. Last night the same. Watched the first half of Italy vs. Ghana in an empty house. Jay rang. He said 'Are you cured-from-cancer yet?' which is at least better than opening with 'Hi, cancer-guy!' (To be fair to him, he hasn't said this in a while.) Sort of concentrated on what he had to say, but not really. Watched a recording of some World Cup highlights. Impressed by the Czech Republic. Their manager looks like Roman Polanski.

Later

Have been in to see Felicity Carr. Got soaked on the way with Tats, who decided as the heavens opened that 'the walk would take our mind off things.'

As we walked in to the unit we saw Felicity in the corridor. I knew from her body language that the news would be so-so. It's more than that: it's good.

My tumour has shrunk by a further 5%, but this isn't conclusive enough to say game over. It's more or less what they expected: 'A mass of 1 × 2 cm' is left, which may or may not be scar tissue. The PET scan I was promised a few weeks ago is already booked for Monday, at Mount Vernon of all places, a stone's throw from where I grew up. This will tell us if there's anything living left: if there is I'll have a course of 3 weeks' radiotherapy before the summer hols. If not, we're done. Then the three-monthly checks.

Felicity and Carol were cheery, confident, but not really nailing colours to the mast. I heard myself begin one question with 'I know it's hard for you to say, but . . .' which is as good as not expecting an answer.

What do I feel? What did I expect?

The really interesting part of the exchange with Felicity was, as ever, when she referred to knowledge she'd had all along, but not actually disclosed. Specifically, she described my original tumour-size as 'huge'. No one has described it thus until now. (For the record, 'huge' is always how I imagined it, even after a radiologist pooh-poohed it with the words 'we get one's the size of grapefruits: four-by-five's *nothing*.') The policy of gradual disclosure? Yes. The policy of managing disappointment? That would be unfair. Reading between the lines I think she was saying: 'Given how big your tumour was, and how aggressive your cancer is, we're very satisfied to have come this far. Now we need to make sure we can remove the rest of it.' In football speak this translates as 'We would have taken removing 95% of it before half-time.'

It's a beautiful sunny evening.

But I still have cancer.

All of this was put into perspective later as we sat waiting for an X-ray on my back (Felicity wondered if my pain is referred from my vertebrae). There was a lady there being comforted by a hospital chaplain.

In a voice we couldn't help hearing she told him how her husband had 'had a turn which we thought was a stroke.' She described how she left him to walk round the block with the dog. When she got back she found him sprawled on the patio with blood pouring out of his head. After they got him to hospital they found a massive tumour in his brain, with further shadows on his lungs. They had had no idea.

I had seen him being wheeled in as I emerged from my changing cubicle. He was jolly but completely incoherent. 'And now,' his wife sniffed, 'we'll have no Maurice.'

As I walked back to my cubicle after the X-ray I heard the priest administering the last rights to him in the corridor.

Duncan took my hickman line out earlier.

While I was in there Tatty talked to Dave, a patient we've seen on the wards on and off since the day I was originally given my scan-result-bad-news.

He's deep into his second round of E-SHAP, the relapse treatment I had been briefly promised.

He was diagnosed with lymphoma over 2 years ago, had CHOP-R and then recovered. He's done one round of E-SHAP already, but the tumour has shrunk insufficiently for them to move onto the bone marrow transplant. He'll be in every day this week, and the pump he wears over his shoulder, cased in what Tatty calls 'the handbag', gives him a further week of zapping while he's at home. He never takes it off. A week ago they kept him in a whole week when his hickman line got infected.

Before him, he told Tatty, his father had had the same cancer, and his father before him. They both died from it. His grandmother, too.

Wednesday 14 June

Shim and I stared at the ceiling talking again last night.

'Dad, why do you need another scan?'

'Well, this one can tell if there's any living cells on my cancer or not.'

'And what if there is?'

'If there is, then I'll have three weeks of radiotherapy. It's not as bad as chemotherapy, apparently, it's like having sunburn.'

'How is it like that?'

'They shoot radioactivity at you and it leaves your skin a bit burned, I suppose.'

'Does it have a green light?'

'Yup.'

163

'What, like a laser gun?'

'Yup. Actually, no, it's not like a laser gun.'

'What's it like then?'

'Well, a gun, kind of, a machine, I mean. Which shoots radioactivity at me.'

'Can they use them in wars?'

'No, and anyway, they wouldn't be much use because it's not like a bullet, which wounds you instantly. Radioactivity takes time.'

'So it wounds you then?'

'Well, a little, but it gets rid of the cancer more, or what's left of it anyway.'

'And how can this scan tell if there's anything left?'

'Don't know really. It just can, that's all. They told me that often with my kind of cancer there's a lump left at the end. Usually it's just dead.'

'Dad, would you rather have a million pounds or be cured from cancer?'

'Be cured from cancer.'

'Wouldn't you want the money?'

'No, I want to be well again.'

'But couldn't the money help make you better?'

'Not necessarily. And anyway, I trust the NHS.'

'Is the NHS making you better?'

'Yes. It is.'

'But wouldn't you want the money?'

'What's the point of having a million quid if you're not well enough to enjoy it?'

'Do you pray every night?'

'No, not every night. Do you?'

'Most nights. I ask God to make you better and to help mum with her work.'

'I pray a bit in the day. Short prayers, like: "Please God, make me better, Amen."'

'Is that all you say?'

'It's all I need to say.'

I keep going back over Tuesday's events. Felicity was upbeat about only one thing, as I remember, my return to work: 'You'll want to get back to your life again.' I didn't really want to hear this; I've got very used to drifting through my days and long not to have to relinquish them.

They have moved my stem cell harvest as well. Karl rang the day after (he's back, looking well, full of banter) to say he and Felicity had had a chat and felt that I'd have a better chance of producing enough cells if they waited till September. I took it at face value, but couldn't help wondering if their chat had also touched on the possibility of me needing to have radiotherapy in a couple of week's time, hence the delay of the harvest. I felt it was his way of saying more treatment was probable, rather than possible. Hence Felicity's rather determined effort not to appear too definite on Tuesday.

Have felt very flat since. Listless. I do drift through the days now. A bit of email. A bit of reading. A text. And all the time thinking when will it be over, can't it be over yet?

Yesterday Shim told me before going out to tennis that the *Express & Echo* came to interview him and the other kids at school for Father's Day. He told me: 'I said the best thing about you was talking to you on my way to school and even though you're really ill you still come with me.'

In the mirror today I noticed something I haven't seen since February: a single black nasal hair, curling round the edge of my left nostril. I looked up at my eyebrows. Next to the half dozen or so wiry old stragglers, a thin line of new growth, about a millimetre in length, in a perfect arc along the pale trench where my eyebrow used to be. Eyelashes too. Next to my three remaining ones, tiny little lashes, almost invisible, now rim my eyes.

I'm shaving every other day now, the growth on my chin as coarse as Desperate Dan's. When I wet my face in preparation I feel as though I am pushing iron filings around my cheeks.

Tuesday 20 June

My favourite World Cup quote so far: Florent Malouda, the French midfielder, speaking after his piles operation: 'All my troubles are behind me now . . .'

Wednesday 21 June

Phoned up Granny on her 100th birthday and we all sang to her. I hope she heard it. After calling me Julian she said 'The thing is, I feel surrounded by love. I'm sure it's what you've been feeling as well.'

Granny never says much to me, but always seems to get to the point straight away. Already feeling nervous about the weekend away at Lymington with everyone.

I can hear the conversations now:

'Anthony, so good to see you. How are you?'

'I'm fine.'

'But how are you *really*?'

PET stands for 'Positron Emission Tomography'. I quote from the Mount Vernon leaflet:

> It uses radioactive substances to look at the way organs work in a unique way. Most of the PET tests performed at Mount Vernon include injection of FDG, a relative of glucose. The scanner looks at cross sections through the body, so the resultant images may be compared directly with the multislice CT or MRI scans performed in the department or elsewhere.

It omits to say that the scan is performed by the grumpiest man in the universe.

The man in the white coat obviously had a taxi waiting for him outside, or perhaps the FBI, so keen was he to get me down the corridor.

As we entered the room – more like a cupboard – for my

injection I asked if I could go to the toilet. 'Well, as quick as you can, please, we are running behind, you know.'

'It never takes that long,' I tried to assure him.

As I settled onto the bed for the shot, he began making excuses for the delay without the crucial ingredients of a smile or an apology.

He is the first person since January not to say 'sharp scratch' as a formality when placing a needle in my vein.

'What's that?' I said, nodding at the transparent cylinder he was taking out of a blue metal box with radioactive stickers.

'Oh, that's your injection.'

'But what's that thing? Around it?'

'Well, it's a radioactive material we're injecting you with.' he said, as if speaking to a six-year-old, 'And that protects us as we inject you.'

'Very clever.'

'Indeed.'

'How much is in there?'

He sighed. He obviously isn't used to six-year-olds.

'About half-a-mill.' A flicker of a smile crossed his face.

Suddenly we were done.

'You've brought your book, I see, but I don't want you reading just yet. I want you to lie down and finish drinking this water.'

He handed me a plastic beaker, filled to the 300 ml mark, and a cup.

Then he vanished, presumably to tell the taxi driver he had a room full of patients to see.

After ten minutes I was shown into another room/cupboard where I was allowed to read. I was asked to take off my watch. After twenty minutes I was asked to 'empty my bladder' then shown into the PET room by a very smiley woman in another white coat who made me comfortable on the familiar ironing board.

The PET-board is even longer than a CT one, with arm rests above your head. She placed a pillow on there 'so they don't dig in', and one under my head. 'It takes a bit longer than CT, you see.' She produced a wedge-shaped piece of hard foam, to go in the space under my knees, placed a white hospital blanket over my legs and tummy, and strapped some white flaps of ribbed material, which had been hanging off the ironing board, across my waist. 'To give us a good picture,' she smiled. 'Right, are you comfortable, Mr Wilson?'

'Very.'

'One last thing, could you undo your zip and lower your shorts to your knees, so the metal isn't picked up?'

'That's lovely.' She smiled again. 'The thing to remember is to keep as still as possible. There's no special breathing involved, and no more injections. Just try and relax. It takes twenty to twenty-five minutes.'

The main difference between PET and CT is the size of the polos. If a CT scan is one giant polo, PET is three. This makes it more like a tunnel. I was glad of the rug they gave me; it was chilly in there. I spent most of the time with my eyes closed trying to remember my Alexander Technique from twelve years ago in Clapham High Street.

Once again, like a good episode of *Dr Who*, it felt simultaneously utterly cutting edge and as though it had been made for 10p.

The ironing board slides you in and a loud whooshing noise happens. Then you slide out the other end, for about a second, before going back in. The machine goes: 'Beeeeeeegshshshe.' In the same direction it slides you halfway back out then stops. For five minutes you lie there, trying to separate your vertebrae without moving a muscle and wondering if they have all gone off for a coffee. Then it whirrs into action, sliding you six inches into the tube, where it stops. Another five minutes passes. You go six inches the other way. It goes on like this for another fifteen minutes, backwards and forwards, at which point you are about to nod off, so completely are your vertebrae relaxed.

Then from nowhere the door flies open and grumpy-white-coat-man enters saying 'That's it' and indicating the chair where your things are. Next to it you notice an old ghetto blaster and a rack of CDs. You feel cheated to have missed out on the chance to listen to the Carpenters, or Jeremy Vine while in the polo. But mainly you feel relief to be out of there, and on the way home.

Thursday 22 June

No scan results yesterday. None today so far. I rang Karl earlier on the ward and he got Helen, Felicity's secretary, to chase for a fax off them. It's 2.15 now. Still nothing. Watched a lot of telly this morning, after dropping Shim off, mostly old *Frasiers*. Then emails. Then more telly. Have settled to nothing.

Luckily I had Shim's sports day to distract me – his last ever at primary school.

They had been given the use of the Royal Deaf School playing field and it was nice to step out of the house for an hour and a half following them round on their circuit of activities. They divide them up into four teams: red, blue, yellow, green. Shim was in yellow.

Some of the games were truly Beckettian: dribbling a ball round markers on the long, pitted grass in a relay; aiming a ball at some cricket stumps from 15 yards, also in a relay. Shim does best at running. He was beautiful to watch, all purpose and concentration and flow in the hurdles, and later in the individual sprint.

The latter was the last event of all, after the individual hurdles, and was played out in front of the whole school and all the parents. He told me in his modest way as we walked to school that he had been picked from his class to represent them in the race, but I could tell he wanted me there.

His race was the last one of all. He came a valiant second. He led for the first 20 yards, but was overhauled, and lost by a yard. No shame. My main emotion, after pride, was nerves. As the build-up to the race grew longer I realised both my knees and my hands were shaking.

As he ran back to take his place with his class he held his hand out for a high-five, which I took to mean he was glad I had come.

Then the teachers asked for quiet and for the parents to gather round for the prize-giving. I hadn't seen the scores, so had no idea of the result, but the cups on the table, with coloured ribbons already tied to them, gave it away.

What I hadn't realised until this point was that Shim had been wearing a yellow bib to denote his status as one of the team captains (there were three for each team).

As he went up with his classmates to collect the winning trophy, I realised I was still shaking, and close to tears. They shook hands awkwardly with the PE teacher, then, as if they had rehearsed it, held the trophy aloft, each with one hand, jumping up and down, for all the world like Brazilians lifting the World Cup.

A man I know, but haven't seen since my diagnosis, came up to me in between races. A really nice guy, someone we've had supper with. He knew I was ill. He really hoped I was getting better, he said. Then he said the most stupid thing I have heard all year: 'I've been meaning to ring you.'

I took this to mean: 'I really wanted to ring, but didn't because I was embarrassed and afraid. Anyway now I've seen you I won't ring any more, or will still not ring, only now you know that I won't. Which is what I wanted: for you to know I knew without having to speak to you. Sort of.'

Later

Still no news.

Waiting days are the worst. Somehow the last CT wasn't so bad because I was booked in to see Felicity so knew I wouldn't be arsed around. The wait over Easter was agony, looking back; I'm glad now, that we had a houseful of family in Scotland to take our mind off it. Desperate to know something before we take off to Lymington for Granny's birthday weekend. Am determined not to play ball with the 'How are you *really*?' crew.

I have two blood 'splinters' remaining on my fingernails. Each treatment is marked in a little wave, some of which have become deep grooves.

On my left forefinger and thumb there's a classic dip, with just a hint of surface flaking. But my right forefinger, thumb and index are a mess (these perhaps because they bore the brunt of my camping burns 18 years ago). It looks as though someone has hit them with a hammer, but painted out the bruising.

Two or three millimetres from the top of each nail begins a curved jagged crack, with the new nail, pink and soft, emerging underneath. On my thumb it's possible to see two or three layers of dead nail exposed as the new growth takes over. It is not pretty.

Noticed last night that the verucca on my left foot, which disappeared during chemo, has come back. The wart on my left forefinger seems to have gone for good, however.

A neighbour said to me she heard a talk on cancer for her work the other day. It included the line: 'You can get your holiday photos done in an hour, but to find out if you've got cancer takes at least a week.'

It occurs to me that when they ring I'll be finding out the most important news of all, as when I was diagnosed, at home.

As I did then I'll be standing, with a cordless phone in my hand, probably in the middle of something but now looking out of the window, the weather now sunny, and a new growth of scaffolding on a house down the street.

I'll be upstairs I should think, probably watching telly, having just hit the remote button. Suddenly the planet will be very still, but for a bird singing somewhere, or a car starting up. And they will tell me, quickly.

And whatever they say I will say thank you, as I always do, and ask about what comes next. Then I will phone Tatty and sound will return to the day, just in time for *Frasier*, or coffee.

Friday 23 June

It doesn't happen like that of course.

Your parents ring you. Then your wife. You ring the hospital in exasperation, and are put on hold, not like in a call centre, with acoustic ambient music to listen to, but with the phone plonked down on the desk. I could hear the drug infusion machines beeping bing-bong, bing-bong in the background, and felt suddenly sick. Then Karl's voice, from a few yards away: 'I think what we'll do is . . . and then . . . so we'll see you on . . . is that OK?' Tantalising. Then a nurse talking about last night's football. Then laughter. Phil came back on to reassure me he was coming really. Then utter silence. More ward noise. Then suddenly Karl.

He was guardedly optimistic.

'It looks like good news,' he began. 'We can't be certain until Wednesday, when we've met with the radiologists, but it looks like it might be clear.'

'OK.'

'You've got what's called 'low uptake', which might be just inflammatory material left over. If it's still lymphoma it tends to be high uptake.'

'OK.'

'So you are probably clear to be deemed in remission, and probably won't need radiotherapy.'

'OK.'

'But as I say, the radiologists are really the ones who know how to interpret these pictures. So we won't know for sure until Wednesday afternoon.'

'What time?'

'We meet from 2–3, so give me a ring at 3.30 and I'll let you know.'

'OK.'

'The thing is, if there's any doubt, you will have radiotherapy. What we don't do is under-treat you and then for it to come back in six months.'

'Yes. Quite.'

'So, I'll speak to you next week. Have a good weekend, Anthony.'

A kind of limbo-ish feeling, but with good grounds for optimism. This is only the second time the word 'remission' has been used. And the first time was to name what I didn't have. I haven't exactly ordered champagne from my wine merchant, nor gone on a 1-click spree, but neither am I sobbing into my shoes.

Feel odd. If it is remission, why still these vestiges of pain in my side?

Spoke to Tats and we agreed it was good news but in light of the meeting of the Wilson clan later, that we'd keep it to 'guarded optimism' rather than 'probably remission.' 'It isn't hard news,' I said to Daddy on the phone, 'so we won't be phoning round. Not 'til after Wednesday anyway.'

Tuesday 27 June

Felicity has called. She repeated much of what Karl had said – that there was low uptake on the scan and that the news was more good than bad – but the angle, the tone, felt different.

A key oncologist cannot make tomorrow's Multi-Disciplinary meeting (MDT) and so they won't be discussing me now until next Wednesday, 5 July. He really needs to be there, she said, because he is the expert at interpreting results such as mine. I said, fine.

Then she laid out in front of me what she thought would be happening next 'in the most likely scenario'. This is that I will probably have another PET scan in 2 months' time, followed up with a short course of local radiotherapy. She explained how with my kind of lymphoma the end of the treatment can be difficult to manage because they are often unsure as to how cancerous the tumour remains.

'If you had a lump on your neck, for example, we would biopsy it straight away as we would know. But in your case it's just so inaccessible – even more so, now it's smaller – that that isn't an option. Very rarely do we operate, but that carries quite a risk, so normally we don't. You see, what I'm trying to avoid is having to give you aggressive chemotherapy – E-SHAP – which would be like using a sledgehammer to crack a nut; at the same time I don't want to under-treat you and for it to return in six months' time.'

She finished the conversation – after I had told her that I'd just seen my entire family – by saying that I could tell them that the news was 'very good', that I am in 'partial remission, maybe complete remission'.

It's too much of a mouthful. All I am saying to them is 'They're cautiously optimistic, but will probably need to do another scan.' After a bit more questioning Felicity said that even if they think my remission is more than partial, they will do a PET scan in a couple of months, to be sure.

She's writing to me so that I can mull it over ('Is it clear as mud?' she said) before next week's meeting. Later I'll be getting it as a fax. When I told Tatty all of this at lunchtime yesterday she seemed happy enough. But later, when Non rang to wish her happy birthday the question moved to 'Why don't they just start radiotherapy straight away, if they think they want to be safe – so that it doesn't grow back?' This is a good question. To settle it, and for Tats to hear it directly from Felicity herself, we've booked ourselves in for a chat at 5 this afternoon.

As we sat in Wagamama's for Tats' birthday meal last night we told the kids the latest, although it hardly felt like news of any consequence.

'Does this mean you're getting better?' they said.

'Yes. But I'm not better completely. Not yet.'

174

'They want to use radiotherapy on me to make sure I don't-'

'To make sure you don't die?' said Shimi.

'Yes, to make sure I don't die.'

Very very very frustrated.

I long to be able to send a magical email to the whole world using the word remission, but dare not. Saw four colleagues for lunch yesterday – I didn't understand any of the gossip, and was at least five seconds behind all the jokes – and couldn't tell them any news, relying on the already well-worn phrase 'They'll know in a week' to head off more close questioning. Playing for safety? Most definitely. I felt guilty, especially as I know that next Wednesday may bring no more information than I have now.

I think Felicity is very keen to be seen to be transparent – and not rushing into announcing a result – which I am grateful for. The subject of her call was really one of preparing me not to expect my treatment to be over until after the summer. I'm sure of that. I can feel myself starting to worry about work – all the crap that needs to be done which I might not be around to do. The frustration of this, and for the first time, the feeling of guilt which goes with (unintentionally) dumping on others. But then, I keep reminding myself, I have cancer. It's not like it's serious or anything.

I had an epiphany to this end last night in the restaurant.

Just staring into space and idly thinking how beautiful my family were and how I consider them my main achievement in life, it suddenly hit me like never before: cancer can kill you. Until now I've thought of it almost on a local level, as something serious which is only possible to deal with by taking each step as it comes: diagnosis, chemo, side effects, scan, results, news, chemo, side effects, scan, results, news etc. In other words, by forcing yourself not to look too far ahead – by focusing on your beautiful family, for one thing. But suddenly, three or so weeks after finishing being treated, feeling better, having the odd drink, eating cheese and olives again, I find myself wanting to be cured *now*, wanting my energy to return NOW, please, impatient that it isn't over, that the 'light at the end of the tunnel' seems to keep receding. What hit me – and I know this will sound really stupid – is that unless the doctors remove my cancer now, it will come back and kill me. Not having allowed myself to consider the final stages of treatment before, I'd not thought through the necessity for it to be successful, having always assumed it would be. Now that there's some doubt as to what the results mean it's finally become clear to me that you don't move from treatment to remission just like that. Instead, you move from certainty that you have a nasty disease, to good progress with the cure, to needing to be certain about the cure, to needing to be even more certain about the cure, and only then using words like remission. It's like chopping a salami in half, then three quarters, then seven eighths, then chopping that final eighth into sixteenths then thirtyseconds (or whatever they're called), each smaller slice taking you paradoxically nearer to being cured but further away from a definite answer. That's where I am now. What hit me is that whether you've got a whole salami in your hand or a slice the size of your finger-nail, you still have cancer and it can still kill you. I still have cancer. They haven't cured me. Yet. I can still die from this.

And then our food arrived, steaming and delicious.

Wednesday 28 June

A sunnier day than it started. Am sitting upstairs with the Walkman, having farted around on the laptop all morning, checking emails, re-checking them, looking at bands on the internet, wondering how to buy music online, generally killing time. Would Virginia Woolf have written *The Waves* if she'd had the web to play with? Probably.

Went to bed early last night. Saw Felicity with Tatty at 5. We began with the letter she's written to my GP, telling him that

I am in 'a very good partial remission.' Which is better than no remission at all. Or relapse. But still not as good as plain old remission on its own.

Quoting the PET scan report she says: 'There is only very low-grade uptake seen associated with a small amount of retroperitoneal soft tissue abnormality, much more likely to represent sequelae of treatment rather than persistent active disease.' First we had to get past 'retroperitoneal' and 'sequelae'. I guessed that sequelae meant 'following on from' but did not understand what it meant in the sentence. Felicity said it meant that it was more likely that the uptake on the scan was as a result of my treatment, going right back to my biopsy, than the continued presence of cancer cells. Retroperitoneal means the muscle wall which the gut hangs from, roughly speaking. So: there is a bit of soft tissue left, but it's quite likely it isn't cancer. This is where it gets interesting, where you find, as Felicity put it, that medicine is not an exact science. And where you find the doctors taking educated guesses, albeit ones with lots of letters after their names.

Essentially they can't be sure that my cancer has gone. They are pretty sure, but not 100% sure. Which means, actually, I still have cancer. When I spoke to Felicity on the phone she was all for waiting for a bit, doing another PET scan, then blasting me with radiotherapy. Tatty and I wanted to ask if I couldn't have the radiotherapy sooner than that, given that my disease is/was so aggressive.

Tatty spoke up first and looked distinctly wobbly. I think Felicity hadn't reckoned on us wanting it over this desperately; nor on the level of anxiety that Tatty displayed. There are all sorts of good reasons, she told us, for not wanting to give me radiotherapy: the potential damage to other organs (e.g. saliva glands in the neck – I thought straight away of John Diamond), the link to problems in the future (e.g. breast cancer – not likely in my case), and the way radiotherapy is increasingly being cut back on as much as possible (not for reasons of expense) because of complications.

But Tatty pressed on, looking more and more wobbly. To her credit, Felicity listened really well, taking every opportunity to say how pleased she was with my progress and that she would be putting our views very strongly forward at next Wednesday's MDT.

I'd like to think that we'll get the green light – ho ho – for some radiotherapy in the next two weeks, with a CT/PET scan sometime around the end of August. It'll mean the summer hols will be buggered up a bit, but I'd rather have that than a delayed return to work in September.

Speaking of which, Occupational Health have been in touch and are talking about negotiating a 'graded return': 'The most important thing is getting well, not what your colleagues think.' Hurrah. I don't want to go back to work on September 1st full-time in any case. Apart from being terrified, I don't feel up to it. A 'graded return' sounds like the right thing. The future has a bit more shape to it, perhaps. As we drove away from the hospital I said to Tats 'If this summer is buggered up, why don't we throw some money at Christmas?' 'Or next summer?' she said. 'We could go to the States.' 'Or do what Andy did in Canada,' I said. 'Vancouver Island, a bit of camping, then the city. How about it?'

I offered her a drink when we got in, but she didn't want one. I made do with a San Miguel. It occurs to me, after my hangover on the weekend – Paracetamol at 6 am! – that my resistance to alcohol has been permanently affected by my treatment. First, I find now I can drink again that I can't resist having one, ha ha. Second, while I feel like drinking a case, I find I am able to have only a single drink without feeling dreadful the morning afterwards. I can see a future of watching other people getting pissed at parties and toasting myself at book launches with Perrier, Raymond Carver style. Still, if that's what it takes. It's funny, having cancer. What was previously unthinkable suddenly becomes quite viable (forgive the pun). Normal, even.

Later

As we sat waiting for Felicity yesterday a woman called Wendy came and sat down with her husband. She immediately burst into tears. She had come from the direction of the ward, or perhaps one of the consulting rooms. 'I just wish I could die,' she gasped, collapsing onto a row of soft chairs. 'All I do all day,' she said to the auxiliary nurse who had come over to comfort her, 'is lie down. That's all I do. All day. For the last fortnight. It's dreadful.'

As the auxiliary handed her a new supply of cardboard sick-bowls she ran through her list of side effects. Tatty whispered to me: 'She's still got her hair, though. And her eyebrows.' This was true. If we'd been sitting next to her on the bus we wouldn't have thought of her as a cancer patient at all. But in the Haematology waiting room, reeling off a list of complaints and clearly fatigued, she looked as vulnerable as anyone I've sat next to on a drip in a headscarf. As we left Tatty whispered to me again: 'Thank you for being positive. I couldn't have put up with that.'

'I didn't feel I had a choice,' I said.

Thursday 29 June

Tatty off work with a dodgy tummy. Spent the morning bringing her marmite toast and peppermint tea, then lying on the bed chatting staring at the ceiling. I tried not to think about going back to work. She picked it up immediately and asked what was on my mind.

I'd just had an email, I said, which I needed to answer yesterday, to order books for my students for next year. We spent the next half an hour pricing the list up from Amazon, titles like *Teaching Fiction Writing at Key Stage 2*. There's a Ronseal title if I ever saw one. I ought to do one for poetry.

How often have I said that in the last year? Does cancer make me more or less likely to get on with these projects?

Then I told Tatty that I was projecting forward to everyone expecting me to be 100% straight away and that it frightened me. She said that cancer has changed me – forced us all to look at our priorities really clearly. And that I had realised that work wasn't everything, at least not the everything we are so used to stressing over. 'If you do lose your job,' she said, 'which I doubt, you're really good at what you do, you know, but if you do, it isn't the end of the world. You know that now.'

'I suppose so,' I said. 'Being terminally ill with six months to live, that's the end of the world.' I paused to look at her. 'And even then, it's not.'

'No, that comes when you've gone,' she said.

A new condition for me to get used to: scoliosis, curvature of the spine. When Felicity was examining me a couple of weeks ago before my PET scan she felt around my lower back for a second. 'Do you have any back trouble?' She said. 'How did you know?' I said. 'It's a bit soft in there,' she said. 'I think we need an X-ray of your spine.'

The results came back straight away, but were forgotten in the post-PET discussions. She read them out to me again on Tuesday. 'So when are you having your next bone density scan?' I told her it had been four or so years since the last one, so might be due for one soon. 'It seems to be a bit ad hoc,' I smiled. 'Ask your GP then,' she said.

I went in to see him today. I mentioned the scoliosis, talked him through the PET results, and slipped in that I was still having some pain on my side. He looked surprised, but humoured me with an examination. 'As you know,' he said afterwards, 'my own theory was that your pain came from the pressure of your tumour on your urethra, or on some nerve tissue. So I did expect it to go away. Your kidney is fine, by the way. I suggest we wait and see. And if it persists or gets worse then come back. Of course.' He looked at me a bit blankly, reddening slightly. 'Of course, this means, this might mean, I mean, that it was coincidence we found it at all. Because you weren't ill to speak of, symptoms-wise, I mean. It's one of those funny things.'

Saturday 1 July

World Cup quarter-final day. All to play for.

Everyone in town or at the beach. Shim on the annual dads-and-kids weekend, this year a bargain-basement deal in a field near the surf, after last year's £200/person effort which I boycotted. I'm meeting Tats and Bendy in a minute for a posh lunch to say well done for her report and for the prize the school have awarded her for 'achievement'.

Further proof of life having moved on whilst I have been ill came later that evening. We were on the way out to supper, suddenly panicking into clothes like Hugh Grant at the beginning of *Four Weddings and a Funeral* ('Fuck! Fuck! Shit!') having lost all sense of time during the penalties with Portugal. I put an M&S Toad in the Hole in the oven, switched the alarm clock on for when it needed to come out, and kissed her on the forehead. 'You'll be OK then? We're on my mobile if you need us.'

As we walked up the road to Stella's house I remembered those first days at Hazel's, our child-minder in Brixton, when Merenna would only be calmed down by being placed into the arms of Adam, Hazel's husband, every day for two weeks. And here she was, being left alone for the first time of an evening.

When we came back it was as though she were both child and babysitter. The child had gone to bed but the babysitter was still up. She had closed the curtains, had her laptop out, and was watching a rap video on the Hits channel. 'Hi Dad.'

On a plate on the table lay the empty Toad in the Hole foil tray. Next to it, the box of four chocolate cream éclairs we'd bought her for pudding. She had eaten three of them. 'I'll go to bed in a minute,' she said. 'I'm just finishing watching this.'

As I drove Tats into town earlier I found myself saying to her that I didn't think there was going to be a champagne-popping moment when having cancer will cease. What I predict (and what I said) is that after the (almost certain) radiotherapy there'll be a scan and it will say I am pretty much OK. But it won't be conclusive. They will tell me to go away, to go back to work, and to come back for a check sometime before Christmas. And when I've had that check, which will be inconclusive, I'll be told the same. That check will be OK. 'No signs of activity', they will say. This time they will tell me to come back in six months. That check will be OK as well. 'See you in another six months,' they will say. And so it will go on. There won't be a moment, like getting a book contract, or the letter confirming you have been awarded your PhD, when the project will come to an end. Not for five years, at the earliest. The hardest moment to take will be the one in late summer when they tell me that 'for now, we'll just have to wait and see' which means they won't know if they've got rid of it or not, not for sure, not definitely.

Like red buses, cancer-stories come and go, then reappear in twos. Yesterday was a two-in-a-row day. It began, between World-Cup-Exit-phone-ins, with 5 Live's coverage of the Race for Life in Chiswick. They had an actor from *The Bill* who has been in remission for a little while, and a man whose job it is to train the people who answer the phones at Cancer Research.

It was the most sensible and sensitive discussion, in the right sense of the word, that I have heard on the subject since being diagnosed. This is high praise: I had made yet another bet with myself that within five seconds I'd be ringing in to complain at their used of war imagery. Perhaps it was because they had someone on who had actually been through the treatment; maybe it was the influence of a man whose job is to pay attention to the exact words we use to describe feelings about the disease. Whatever it was, it worked.

Most people who ring up, said the trainer man, just want advice on how to be able to talk about it. 'And these are not always relations,' he said, 'like husbands, wives, brothers and so on. Many of them are just ordinary friends and acquaintances. And all they want is someone to tell them that it's OK, that we all find cancer difficult and frightening.' Is this worth the licence fee? I think it is.

The presenter went on: 'And in that sense, perhaps, cancer is perhaps one of our remaining taboos. Dave, how did you deal with it?'

Dave the actor said two things to this. First, that you need a very robust sense of humour. And that as a cancer patient you want things both ways: the simultaneous desire to be left alone *and* to talk about it. His advice to those close to cancer-patients (no one used the word 'sufferers') was to take each conversation as it came and not to expect too much. 'If they want to offload on you, let them. And if all they want is to gossip and talk about the football, that's great too.' This was also spot on. It cheered me enormously to listen to such a common sense conversation, but saddened me almost the second it was over that it had not gone on for longer ('And now over to Sally for the traffic . . .') and was so rare of its kind: a mainstream radio programme talking about a disease which affects one-in-three of us with calmness, wit and honesty.

Later on, Tats was watching a recorded *Without a Trace* on video. I missed it, preferring instead to read to Shim the latest instalment of Charlie Higson's junior James Bond book. Much later still she asked into the darkness whether I was still awake. I could tell she was crying. 'What is it?'

'It's that *Without a Trace* you missed.' (I had seen a minute of it, so knew it concerned the disappearance of a woman with breast cancer who had been given two months to live.)

'What about it? Was it bad?'

'It's just that. It's just that she disappeared because she felt so strongly that no one had really listened to her while she had been ill, that they hadn't let her be who she was through it all. I was worried that I'd been like that to you.'

In spite of my protestations to the absolute contrary, I wasn't convinced that I had persuaded her of the strength, courage and hope she has given me. If I ever do get to look back on this experience with gratitude, it is the image of Tatty smiling at me as I blinked awake on the ward, after a treatment, saying 'Hello darling. You looked so peaceful while you slept,' which I will treasure most closely.

Sunday 2 July

On the front of the *Observer*, beneath a photo of Wayne Rooney looking up at his red card like a tearful schoolboy I read: 'Farewell Fred: Fred Trueman, legendary Yorkshire and England test bowler, has died at 75.' I thought, but he's only just been diagnosed. Between reading this and finding that the piece on him was by Vic I made another bet with myself that it would be 'after a short battle with etc.' that he had died.

Seeing it was by Vic, and remembering our evening together in Guy and Jemima's garden I quickly cancelled the bet. I shouldn't have. In an otherwise beautiful piece of cricket writing, wry, respectful and lyrical, he opened with the sentence: 'We were in the dining room at Headingley when we heard the grim news that Fred Trueman had died at the age of 75 after a short battle with lung cancer.' Much more accurate, and it keeps the sense of brevity, and suddenness, of the disease. The thing is, if Fred did have a battle with it, it was over pretty quickly, and he came second. I don't think the man Vic describes would have liked being portrayed as a loser. And yet that's what the language does, when it comes to cancer. It kills you, before you even have a chance.

Tuesday 4 July

On the doorstop last night, Robyn. She had come round to say that Merenna would need to catch the bus in the morning, as she and Rory were away. All of a sudden we were having a deep conversation about our cancers. She is now into her second year of remission, and I am (hopefully) about to begin my first.

Just as she had at Budleigh beach, she welled up almost immediately. She told me matter-of-factly that 'It takes about a year before you stop thinking 'Oh, can I do this?', and start feeling normal again'. She went on to say that the worst part of having the disease comes afterwards, 'when you're on your own. It's the bit no one tells you about.'

On Sunday we took my cards down. Since early February they have been collecting on the sill under our bedroom window, a New York skyline of sunsets and flowers. It was Tats who brought it up, though it had been bugging me for a week or two. The mass of them was five or six deep in places, tucked into one another to stop them toppling. Once or twice this has happened, the effect very much like a line of dominoes: it takes seconds to come down and an age to put them back up again. Now we are sticking up the sash for some breeze at night it seemed pointless to go on keeping them there. But it made me think: does this mean I am well now? Or that I am allowing myself to become well? Perhaps the answer is somewhere in the middle. Either way, it seems the end of a chapter, though the cards have been filed away, with all the other documentation I'm not ready to throw out yet.

On taking them down I noticed how many had curled in the sunlight and had had their ink bleached by the same, their messages of hope and offers of favours now faded, so many months after the event.

My fingernails are a real mess, especially on my right hand, which was the one holding the leaking Calor gas canister when I set fire to the inside of a tent eighteen years ago. My thumb and forefinger now have a deep trough in the middle of them as the nail underneath tries to push through. From the side view they make a neat slope for half a centimetre or so, then appear to start growing in a completely new direction. The top edges are all jagged and keep catching on trouser pockets and hand towels etc.

Everyone keeps mentioning my hair, and how much of it I now have: 'like duck down,' as Karl said. I can't tell if it is blonde, as when I was four, the usual brown, or a distinguished post-cancer-trauma grey. We're off for our six-weekly family haircut on Friday, an event I've been sending apologies to. It'll be interesting to see what Hayley makes of me.

One of the stronger aspects of returning hair is my almost rabidly growing moustache. By lunchtime, I have noticed, I now need a shave, like Homer Simpson. Never the most hirsute part of my body, I have become, in the eloquent words of Tatty, akin to 'some Greek waiter.' She is daring me to grow a handlebar over the summer.

I wrote a long email yesterday to Jean, in reply to her question about whether this has changed me at all. I talked a lot about relishing each day more than I did before. And the need to look and listen more, especially to my children. I have come to realise that people are more afraid of cancer (while they are speaking to me) than I am. But the thing which made me do a double take, even though I had written it a thousand times before, is how I signed off: 'Love for now', suddenly realising it was an imperative to make the most of each day whilst realising that each one is so short.

Presence

Sunday 9 July

Morning

No one else up. Sitting here with coffee in the kitchen. Is this what getting better is like? I am not hung-over but my knees hurt like hell. I have just seen eight or nine blue tits on the apple tree looking for insects and darting on and off the bird feeder.

In the middle of all this, a call to my mobile on Wednesday evening, as she said she would, from Felicity Carr. I am going to have 'involved field radiotherapy', as we discussed. The activity on my tumour is 'almost negligible', the MDT has pronounced. 'But even if your scan results were completely negative, we would still have given it to you, just to make sure.' She went on: 'As you had such bulky disease, it's better to be safe than sorry.' It is fascinating how the words 'huge' and 'bulky' crop up, now I'm almost into remission, replacing 'substantial' and 'high-grade'. I don't blame them for retrospectively telling me how dangerous my disease was. After all, you don't greet your new patient with 'You've got a huge tumour there, Mr Wilson, and it's really aggressive!', do you?

The side effects aren't serious, Felicity told me, 'nothing like chemo anyway.'

'What about the tiredness?' I asked her.

'Oh, you might get tired, yes. But tiredness we don't count as serious, just inconvenient.'

So that's what the last five months have been.

Tatty has set me two projects: to make CDs for the car (the first lot all got nicked) and to sort out the photos. The former is a piece of cake: not for nothing do they know me as DJ Ant up at the deli. As far as the latter is concerned, the words

'Augean' and 'stables' come to mind. We are talking about a blue plastic storage box, the kind they used to sell in Habitat, full of photos, undated and unsorted, from the last thirteen years. The last actual album I filled in was one commemorating the birth of Shimi, with Merenna still in nappies. And I must have done that one two years ago, in a rare burst of guilty activity.

You come across a lot of things when you scatter your life over the floor. Me looking twelve on my wedding day. Colislinn, the kids in the stream. The stuff which goes through your mind when you're told you have cancer, as it happens. Several are of Jay and Rosie, holidays we took together in 1992, in France and Norfolk. It goes: Jay and Ant by the Canal du Nord; Jay and Rosie by the Canal du Nord; Rosie and Tatty by the Canal du Nord. Ditto the North Sea in Norfolk. In each one we are smiling the unlined hopeful smiles of the recently married, either at each other or straight to the camera. There is one of Jay with his head on my shoulder. None of us have had children yet, though it was in le Ribécourt that Tatty and I began discussing trying. It was a lot of fun, that holiday.

Tuesday 11 July

In the garden: the raspberries droop earthwards; young apples, no bigger than golf balls, litter the lawn. The lettuce close to being shot. The lavatera are poking through the fence at the front. For the first time in six months I have eyebrows again, perfect dark arcs above each eye, with none of the bleached wiry hairs of old. Young hairs on my arms, too. I haven't tried to drink alcohol for a week now, and feel better for it – I read a story in the paper once about a stand-up comic who gave it up while she wrote her memoirs, because it helped her remain clear-headed. Whatever it takes. What's another two months without it? Or six? Or a year? Or a lifetime? The thing is, you remember everything much better. And enjoy the mornings more. At least I still have coffee.

Yesterday my first two-cup day since Christmas. Partly we were running low on tea, and partly I wanted to see if I could take it. I sailed through, as Karl would say.

The fridge magnet fairies have been back:

> The language is flooded but we
> leave death at luscious leg light.

I love this. It's nonsense, or rather, as Seamus Heaney says about Edward Lear, a *parody* of sense. Leaving death at luscious leg light is, surely, what it's all about, isn't it?

Wednesday 12 July

Not really following my own advice today, or any day this week. I ring the hospital, who say they'll chase my appointment and that a letter will come. It doesn't come. I ring again and they say they'll chase it again and ring me back later. It's a bit like dealing with B&Q.

Meanwhile the nails on my thumbs and index finger are splitting. They're now pulled out of their troughs and have started to curve back towards the ceiling. The thumb in particular is gruesome. The nail underneath is now almost fully grown, making the jagged crescent on top of it loose. It is starting to come away at the sides now. I slide a fingernail from the other hand underneath it to try and prise it off, but it does not want to come. If I catch it on a door handle or kitchen drawer before it falls off I can envisage much blood and cursing.

On my chest, 45° north-east from my nipple, a perfect round scar where my hickman line used to protrude. At a jaunty angle just above it, a scar a centimetre long, where Duncan went in to cut the tube out. Together they make quite a neat exclamation mark.

Thursday 13 July

The hospital rang yesterday. It was a new voice, Clare Murray, the secretary of Dr Perera ('Perry' to everyone who knows him) my oncologist. He's the one who was missing from the MDT two weeks ago, and on whose say-so I'm being blasted. My appointment isn't for two weeks: 26 July. Either they are very confident that there's barely any activity on my tumour, or things have genuinely started to slow down now I've moved from one department to another. Feel a mixture of resignation and frustration. The former because, however scared of going back I am, this effectively puts my return to work back to late September/early October. The latter because we had hoped we would all be done and dusted before going up to Scotland. Have told them I *am* going away, that the holiday is inviolable. This doesn't seem to have fazed them. A distinct lack of rush suddenly.

Friday 14 July

I have chopped off the loose thumbnail which had begun to separate itself from the new one underneath. This revealed, right at the bottom of the nail's now enormous bulge (the trough at the foot of the hill) a groove running right across the nail. It could be the result of some over-eager use of the nail file, but I doubt it. It's much more likely to be my final – and most extreme – beau line from the chemotherapy, evidence that the poison still hasn't quite left the system.

With the fingernail on my right hand in such a chronic state, I've noticed that I'm putting my cash machine cards into my wallet with the raised numbers showing so they are easier to get a grip when I pull them out. It's something I never do, for security reasons, but now find I'm stuck in shops and in queues for minutes on end if I don't.

Monday 17 July

Second week of the heatwave.

We went to see *Twelfth Night* in the park.

The setting was great: Victorian/Edwardian dress, an end-of-the-pier helter-skelter and Punch and Judy box, the latter used to fantastic effect in the box-tree scene. It was one of those shows that bats well all down the order without any-one really stealing it. Closest in this regard came Sir Andrew Aguecheek, resplendent in a Toad-of-Toad-Hall check and blonde wig, all wobbly limbs and permanently nonplussed. He reminded me of an upper class Eric Idle, with all the con-fidence taken out.

Malvolio was good, a sour-faced butler, and a brave deci-sion to play Feste as a seen-it-all busker really paid off.

What really struck me though, was the verse. They all get memorable lines ('Some have greatness' etc.) but best by far are Viola's. It seemed to me that whenever she opened her mouth to say anything it was as if the emotional voltage of the play got switched back on to full. Not that the rest of it is set piece stuff, or treading water, just that Shakespeare really goes under the fingernails when she's around. The willow cabin speech and the duet with Orsino ('a bit like yours, my lord') were simply lovely to watch, and arousing, in the best sense of the word.

Tuesday 18 July

Have padded around the house all day with nothing to show for it. Woke up late so got dressed without bathing in order to play catch up with everyone's breakfasts and packed lunches.

Dropped Shim off then watched telly with the windows open.Then a (cold) bath and a shave. Farted around on email (i.e. deleting ones from work without reading them), then added books to my wish list on Amazon.

No cricket on the radio to kill the silence. There is, as Beck-ett says somewhere, . . . just . . . me. Today is the last one (Merenna breaks up this afternoon) of my life alone during my illness. From tomorrow there will be friends coming round, a different TV channel being watched, more mess. Life.

I realised as I walked Shim to school yesterday, that this was the last week of school-walks, ever. Today he told me 'I've got 24 hours of this school left.' We're all counting them off.

I wonder what it's done to me, this time alone? Even when I taught part-time and wrote my first book of poems for the rest of it, before children, I don't think I've been so consistently on my own, in my own head. I can hardly turn round and say I've used it to work my way through Tolstoy or that I finally got round to *Ulysses*.

Neither can I claim any great insight. As Jane Tomlinson put it in the newspaper the other day, having cancer is shit. People are great, and some days are better than others, but basically, it's a shit time. Let no one tell you otherwise. I wish I could say that I'm wiser for it, or less selfish, or better at listening, though I'd like to be.

All I would say is, I may not use them to the maximum, but I do appreciate each day more, the texture of the air at 7 am, feet on the cold kitchen floor, breeze in at the back door, the mornings of seagulls and cathedral bells. I have also noticed how unambitious I have become. For me, I mean. I'm determined to finish the novel, but if it doesn't work out, it doesn't. Suddenly I feel the same for the poetry. And I never thought I would say that.

What I want is to – to be present. That's what I've learned. I want to strive for presence, now, here in my kitchen, with a Boeing overhead, and later at Merenna's prize-giving as she collects her award. In my writing, as I listen to the music in a line and as my characters cause each other damage. To hear it, feel it and imagine it, as one might the shock of recognition of Thomas putting his hand in the Lord's side. I want that 'deep down sense of things,' to use Hopkins' phrase. The wild cry of shame in Shim's voice when he comes in late and when we aren't even angry with him. The laughter and a candlelit table which is both transitory and timeless. To spot words in Shakespeare plays that you didn't know he used

– 'botched' for example. To watch weird dance and good, meaty thrillers. To walk on Exmouth beach on bracing Saturday afternoons and be rugby tackled by your son and his friend. To use trains. To watch the light take leave of a room. To breathe, and then breathe again, but to notice it.

Wednesday 19 July

In a flash of inspiration yesterday I went onto the net and found a great website which sells both Clairefontaine exercise books – like these, and Lamy fountain pens – like this one. You pick your colour and quantity, send them your email, then ring up with your credit card no. when the confirmation comes through. And it's not in French. They're based in Bury St Edmunds and have sent the books already. In the background I heard a boy shouting. 'Someone has just discovered the *Dr Who* website,' the voice said. 'By the way, if what you want isn't there, just ask and we'll order it.' I can feel a love affair coming on.

Thursday 20 July

7.15, no one up

A great evening last night. Paul and Sally, Claude and Lauren, Steven and Kari. Courgette bruschetta with our drinks, melon from the continental market with Serrano ham from the deli, Ant's famous chicken salad, and raspberries from the garden. Didn't even go near a drink and can remember everything.

Slowly I am realising how much of a crutch it was before I had cancer. Secretly guzzling a glass or two of Chardonnay while cooking before the guests arrived. The constant feeling of worry the next morning that I had shouted or been rude or just crashed out. Tats said over breakfast just now: 'Don't worry, you haven't done that for ages.' I woke this morning feeling exhausted and instantly thinking two things: I'm not hung-over and Did I really behave? As though I haven't yet trained myself to relax and trust that I can get through a supper without being sloshed.

The other thing I noticed, as when I had chemo, was the alcohol on other people's breath. Not that anyone was steaming. It made me faintly nauseous, a kind of chemical memory laid down in the poisoning that I thought I had lost or moved on from. (I was in Spar early in the morning the other day, during the baking-hour, and felt much the same, still, nearly gagging at the cooked pastry smell.)

The reading I did back in June, the Richard Ford novel, turned out to be a false dawn. Stuck at the proverbial p. 63. You get into it, but don't persevere (am I being too harsh on myself?). It is nothing to do with the writing, and everything with my concentration, or lack of. Another book flies across the room.

Saturday 22 July

Has having cancer changed me? I talk a good game of it. But I'm not sure really. Suspicions remain that I am still the same airheaded husband of old. Not malicious, just not very good at listening and doing what I've been asked.

This was made brutally clear to me the other night when Tatty asked: 'Did you get the alcopop and Pimms for my classroom assistants?' I went cold.

Spar was able to help with the Smirnoff, but no joy on the Pimms. I had to make do with a Valpolicella from the wine rack instead.

Tats was explosive, but, considering, quite restrained, reminding me of my utter disregard for her and that my focus remains trained on myself, which is especially selfish as I am hardly busy. I took it on the chin ('Don't even think of saying sorry. "Sorry" isn't good enough.') and stayed quiet for the rest of the evening.

You see, you think you've emerged blinking into a new life of selflessness, where only others' needs come first, but you haven't. You still say to your daughter 'Can you say that again, I missed it?' and to your son 'I can't read to you tonight, I'm too tired'. In the street, meanwhile, you bump into friends and neighbours, and smile. 'Yes, it's going well,' you tell them, 'I'm improving all the time.'

A good conversation with one of Shim's former teachers at the school barbeque the other night. She was saying how a few years ago she had a lump somewhere. It turned out to be harmless. She said: 'It still took a couple of weeks to get the results. I can't describe the feeling of relief when they came through.' I said it must have been a shock, the whole process. 'Well, that's it really,' she said. 'You realise what's important to you. Deep down. You must have had that.' I nodded. 'I've been trying to hold onto that feeling ever since, just of being grateful and determined not to get stressed over the little things.' She paused. 'But it's difficult, isn't it? You tell yourself you're lucky to be alive, but you still get swallowed up by it.'

My lovely Clairefontaine exercise books have arrived from Bury St Edmunds, fresher than fish. Not quite the same as the one I am writing in now, but beautiful nonetheless. This one has a one-and-a-half-inch margin and one centimetre squares filled with four tiny rectangles. My new ones are the classic half-centimetre 'maths squares', right across the page. Stunning colours, too: lime green, and violet. It's quite possible I like writing only because I liked stationery first.

Daddy always used to say 'You really know summer's arrived when it's The Open.'
On the front of yesterday's *Guardian* a picture of Darren Clarke, whose wife is 'critically ill' with cancer. After this tournament he will be playing no golf 'for the foreseeable future' in order to be with her. Good for him.
Further down the piece it describes her 'continuing fight for health', followed by Clarke's claim that she is 'a real fighter

and is battling on.' Winning The Open, or getting well from cancer, which is the tougher? I wondered whether this is what goes through his mind as he makes the turn at one over.

I don't blame Clarke for resorting to war metaphor: that is what sportsmen do. The pressure to describe it otherwise must be overwhelming.

A refreshing antidote to this was to be heard on the BBC2 commentary, by Peter Alliss, famous 'voice of golf'. Alliss is one of those instantly recognisable broadcasters, like Richie Benaud, or even John Peel, who appears to be saying much more than he actually does. In Alliss's case you also have the added benefit of finding out whatever the *Daily Mail* is thinking at any given moment. Mostly I block him out. But yesterday, in a short gap between shots, he was passing on the best wishes of himself and 'the team' to a former green keeper (or such) 'currently suffering from cancer'. I actually thought that was a brave thing to say. We prefer 'the battle' or 'the fight' with cancer, to shy away from the fact that it is painful. Sometimes you do need a member of the gin-and-blazer brigade to cut through the bullshit surrounding a topic to tell it like it is.

Thursday 25 July

One last thought on the above – then I'll shut up. It occurred to me about a day after I'd written it that 'the battle with cancer' is nearly always used in the past tense, i.e. after someone has died. If it *isn't* used in the past tense (as with Darren Clarke's wife) it seems to me it's a shorthand for saying 'losing battle' or, which would be more accurate, 'poor prognosis'. But we can't say 'poor prognosis' because that is to make it sound too fatal, too grim. So we make it into a battle, making it clear we expect the patient to 'give it a good go', even if they cannot, even if that is hopelessly unrealistic. What all this comes down to, as John Diamond says, is the deeply misguided idea that it is the patient's responsibility to get better, not the doctor's. This is such a damaging concept for the culture to go on promoting because it means if the battle is lost it follows that it is somehow the patient's *fault* for dying. It is pure romantic bollocks. The 'fight', real or otherwise, is not glorious, it's bloody exhausting. If you *are* lucky enough to win, it's the doctors who need thanking.

There is having cancer, and there is your Freeview digi-box breaking down. Suddenly we only have four channels to watch. I confess to feeling utterly bereft (though not as bereft as I am at Channel 4 having taken off *Frasier* from its 9.15 a.m. slot just because it's the school holidays). Luckily BBC1 was showing *Billy Elliot*. (I also confess to not feeling over-excited at this prospect, having seen it, and rather agreeing to the '*Kes*-with-tapdancing' tagline it has acquired). It was much better than I remembered it being.

Before it came on, Freeview box RIP, we sat through a *Strictly Come Dancing* special, hosted by Bruce Forsyth, live from Trafalgar Square, a newly-white Nelson's Column looking the other way in the background.

Moving from the 'nation at ease with the foxtrot' (Forsyth) to scenes of the miners' strike in mid-80s Co. Durham was quite jarring. I wondered if five or even ten years ago such an event would have been possible, let alone twenty. It also came to mind as a rather apt metaphor for what we have become: celebrity-obsessed, post-modern-irony-aware, and, of all things, dance-literate. But what do we make? We no longer send miners down into the ground to dig up coal which is too expensive to bring to the surface, let alone use. For all its witty, moving and unsparing laying bare of the masculine psyche, I doubt that the kind of men – and boys – the film portrays could have foreseen a world where it would come to be seen not only as 'normal' but explicitly celebrated to have a job which, in their eyes, involves no 'real work' at all. Watching it I felt intensely proud to be part of a nation which has changed so much, and so quickly. At the same time I couldn't help wondering a) whether it was all just on the surface, and b) what we have replaced the 'traditional' industries with. Your call is in a queue and will be answered shortly.

I think Tats blubbed solidly for the last 20 minutes. The bit that really got me, however, was when Billy has to bring a collection of objects to show his dance teacher (Julie Walters) from which he is to build a dance sequence.

The key object is a letter, written to him by his mother when she knew she was dying, to be opened when he reached the age of eighteen. The advice and the sentiment were simple: 'No matter where you go or what you do, I'll always be proud of you. Find what you are good at and do it. It has been the greatest privilege of all, to have known you. Love, Mam.'

No amount of Bruce Forsyth in a tuxedo can stop you being cut in two by this, especially if, like me, it is exactly the same letter you wrote in your head to your own children three months ago, when you also believed you were dying. Two parallel tears carved their way down my cheeks. I looked across at Bendy to see if she saw me, but she was slouched low on the other sofa, the laptop on her knees obscuring her view.

Wednesday 26 July

Yesterday lunchtime to the hospital to see Felicity, who turned out to be Duncan. A bit of a chat, a bit of an examination, a bit of World Cup banter ('Last time I saw you, you were poking about in my chest during Korea vs. Togo.' 'Yes, it's left a hole in my life.' 'Not like it did in my chest.') and off we go. Three quarters of an hour reading old National Geographics (did you know ravens mate for life?) then ten minutes being seen. The real deal is today, at 2.30, in radiology.

Duncan didn't seem to think there was any real activity left. 'It was a really easy decision at the MDT meeting in the end,' he said. 'We just looked at it [the scan result] and said, Yes, let's blast it a bit. You'll probably only need a couple of sessions.' This was a surprise. Having spoken to Felicity I was expecting 2–3 weeks' worth. Maybe I'll be going back to work sooner that I thought. An elating and terrifying thought.

Later I was up at the uni to ask about my disability pay (my statutory sick pay is about to end). The JobCentrePlus people (Department of Work and Pensions) didn't want the form the uni had sent me and just gave me a pink leaflet with a phone number on it. The uni were nonplussed. I found my way to the office of Velma who I'd spoken to on the phone when the form came through.

She kindly rang the number for me and suddenly I was being formally interviewed, to assess whether I was eligible or not.

My answers went something like:

Yes.

Yes.

Yes.

Yes.

Anthony.

With an 'h', yes.

Wilson.

One 'l'.

Charles.

EX2.

That's right.

Yes.

Yes.

Tatiana.

T-a-t-i-a-n-a.

Wilson.

Yes.

Yes.

I haven't got it on me I'm afraid.

Yes.

Yes.

Yes.
Merenna.
Wilson.
M-e-r-e-n-n-a.
That's right.
Yes.
Yes.
Yes.
Shimi.
Wilson.
Yes.
Aren't they?
S-h-i-m-i.
Correct.
Yes.
Yes.
Yes.
Yes, it's here on my sick note.
First of July to the first of September.
Yes.
Yes.
It's non-Hodgkin's lymphoma. It's a blood cancer.
H-o-d-g-k-i-n-apostrophe-s. Lymphoma: l-y-m-p-h-o-m-a.
Yes.
Yes.
Yes.
No.
No.
I don't know.

'How are you diddly doodling?'

I looked up from my National Geographic article on ravens. It was Faith, an auxiliary nurse for whom the phrase 'larger than life' was probably invented. 'The last time I saw you you were *ill*,' she beamed, referring to my all-day recovery from the procedure to put my hickman line in.

This was no post-Simpsons post-modern attempt at irony. I really *had* been ill then, back in April, officially at any rate, and still under the cosh from the chemo. It's funny how everything becomes relative on a cancer ward. Of course I was ill, you want to say, I wouldn't be here if I hadn't been. What Faith meant was: 'Don't you look well!' Truly, I thought, I have arrived.

Later

Just back from meeting with the oncologist. We met with Dr Nicole McGregor (standing in for Perry), an extremely nice woman, in an office across the corridor from Haematology.

Minutes before, we'd popped in there to hand over a bag of unused drugs, and stood chatting with Gillian, Karl and Nadine in a doorway of the ward. A homecoming of sorts, we bantered about Karl's recent safari-trip photos. We asked after his recent radio treatment: it's been successful.

Tatty noticed immediately the unearthly hush across the corridor in Oncology, the distinct lack of banter in doorways. But Nicole was just that right mixture of old-school bedside manner and modern efficiency. I'm to have four weeks of radiotherapy, probably starting in September (so much for Duncan's two days). The main side effects are cumulative, as we've been told to expect, and they include tiredness, indigestion and irritable bowels. The longer term side effects are anyone's guess: possible long-term kidney damage, and possible malignancy in cells in the radiated area some twenty years hence. But, as she delicately put it: 'We have to deal with the problem in front of us first.'

We asked about returning to work. 'Well, September's out with treatment, then you need a good 2–4 weeks after that. End of October I should think.' Tatty and I looked at each other without speaking: just enough time to miss the Ofsted inspection, we thought.

Nicole left the room to let us peruse the consent form and to try to book in a 'practice scan' (it's tomorrow at 10.15) before we go away. While we sat there trying to decipher her writing I said: 'I suddenly feel mortal again.' 'We are mortal,' she said. 'That's why we have to make the most of the time we have.'

Holiday

Thursday 27 July

To the hospital early this morning for a 'radiotherapy planning scan'. This is using CT equipment (giant polo and ironing board) but without the fasting, drinking disgusting drinks and nausea-inducing injection. Piece of cake. Two ladies come in, ask you to roll up your T-shirt and loosen your shorts. Then you lie on the ironing board and they make three dots on your body with felt tip pens, one below your tummy button and the other two just above your hip bones. (I'm sure I caught one of the ladies taking a peak under my boxers at how far my pubic hair had come back.) Then you slide into the polo for a bit (no injection, no automated voice saying 'Breathe in, breathe away normally') and then out again. The ladies re-emerge from their hidey-hole and draw over the felt tip dots with Windsor and Newton permanent Indian ink which they transform into tattoos by pricking your skin with a sharps needle. 'Some wives leave their husbands when they get one of these, even though it's only a full stop,' one of them says. As you're going they tell you 'We'll see you again on the 18th August, for a treatment verification meeting. It'll be about half an hour. We'll go through the whole thing then, including side effects. Treatment should start end of August/ beginning of September. See you then.' Then you're out of there, 15 minutes from start to finish: exactly what it says on the appointment card.

Yesterday Nicole described the radiology machine as 'a giant hairdryer which can zap you from above and below.'

'Like something out of *Dr Who*?' I said.

'If you like. It's on a swivel, so it can spin round and zap your back, without you having to roll over on your tummy.'

It made me think: Did they have this kit, ten, twenty years ago? What did they do then?

Lying in the polo again today, while trying to take everything in, I caught myself rather revelling in the attention. No sooner had this thought faded than I once again longed for everything to be over. It won't be, not during the holidays, not in September, not even when I next see Felicity again, in mid-October. I still have cancer, but feel better than I have done since February.

Monday 7 August

At Colislinn.
Everything good.

Have begun trying to read again: *American Short Stories Masterpieces*. Some of the best quality stuff you would want to find anywhere. 'Fever' by Raymond Carver a favourite so far, though the opener, 'Sonny's Blues' by James Baldwin completely took my head off. I see it is as a series of vital set pieces: a passage about brothers, a passage about race, a passage about drugs, and the climax passage about jazz. It is as though the piece itself is jazz, beginning slowly and thoughtfully, and gradually building in intensity until you almost cannot bear to continue reading, mesmerising, poetic and sad.

A Scandinavian jazz CD in the dining room. Coffee. My girls bouncing in from a shopping trip – baseball boots with sequins for Bendy, and a new rucksack.
    Then lunch in the garden: salad, cheeses, humous, crudités, wine for the grown-ups, J2O for me. Newspapers litter the table and the lawn. Conversation: about whether or not to have a moustache-growing competition and Jena saying 'Did you lose your hair *everywhere*?' Tats' reply: 'He lost his pubes, if that's what you mean.'

Cricket in the garden with the boys (one lost ball so far), badminton net bulging in the breeze, swimming in the river. People reading chunks of the *Guardian* out to each other;

swimwear drying on the lawn; housemartins overhead, miniature spitfires. All of the advantages of being in the Dordogne – heat, spending half the day in pyjamas – without actually having to get out there. I'm on the verandah steps and can see GK Chesterton's *Autobiography* and Ian McEwan's *Atonement* lying next to each other in the sun. It probably doesn't mean anything.

It's very, very good to be alive.

Wednesday 9 August

Sally and Paul arrived late last night, given their flight was delayed due to an imposter. Not some Al-Qaeda fanatic, but an old lady trying her luck on the Newcastle flight. Lots of banterly speculation that it was Piers Morgan's mum going for a terror-on-internal-flight scoop.

Before that, the drive with Tats – our first, weirdly, when you think of all the years we've been coming here – to Edinburgh airport to drop off Bendy for her unaccompanied minor flight back to Ex so she can attend her festival. They call them 'U mins' (unaccompanied minors). In the context of being up at the house it was a defining coming-of-age moment. There was my little girl, who only five minutes ago was celebrating her first birthday here on the lawn, suddenly grown-up and nervously making her first big journey on her own. Her next birthday, in three days, marks the threshold into the teenage years. She will spend it without us, in a field with friends and loud music, eating cake from a shop. I hope someone remembers to buy her candles.

We had about an hour to kill at the airport. We mooched around Global News (i.e. Smiths), Bendy ogling uninterestedly little Pentel gift-boxes for £4.99 comprising a gel pen, two biros, a clicky-clicky pencil, a ruler and what they now call 'eraser' – she was especially taken with the 'World's best Jock' socks and plastic mooing cows with 'authentic farmyard noises', a sure reminder that she is still a child, entertained by worthless tat.

She went over to look at the magazines and I looked at books by Gloria Hunniford, on her daughter Caron Keating, who died of breast cancer, and Lance Armstrong, the cyclist and cancer-survivor. I looked at each extremely cursorily, almost giddily anticipating the moment when I would first encounter the words 'brave' and 'battle'. I didn't wait long, needing to look no further than the blurbs. It has taken me all this time to realise it, but what the culture seems to demand is bravery from cancer patients *whether they die or not*.

Again, I'm sure this must be a coping mechanism. If the person in question does die (e.g. Keating) at least we can console ourselves that it was a brave death. I wonder if this is another way of saying 'unfair', which is possibly connected with the fact she was attractive, talented, had two lovely boys and a famous mum. But it's unfair, whoever gets ill. There are mums on housing estates bringing up two boys with no partner and no famous relations who are equally brave, but who have no one to tell their story.

If we fail to say she was brave, therefore, it is as though we are saying she deserved it or, slightly less harshly, that she wasn't very tough. 'At least she was brave,' we say, momentarily feeling better.

The problem with 'brave' is that it's a word designed to make the observer or commentator feel better, not the patient. Also, it obliterates complexity. I'm sure there were days when Keating was brave. But I'm also sure there must have been days when she wanted to curl up and for it all to be over, one way or another. I know this because this is what I have felt.

People have told me I am brave, to face what I have, especially the bad news phase. But brave isn't what I felt. Shit is a word I would use. And overwhelmed, when I stop to think about it. The rest of the time I try to enjoy what's in front of me. Is that brave? I don't think so. It's somewhere between common sense and determination. But don't call me brave.

Brave is, actually, what Lance Armstrong did. The blurb gets it right. But it still leaves me unsatisfied, even though I remain respectfully in awe of his achievements. (What I

210

hadn't realised until picking up the book is that his testicular cancer was stage 4 – yikes.) It is as though we say: 'Well, Lance Armstrong, he decided to fight it, and not only did he beat it, but he won the *Tour de France* to boot. Fighting a disease must really work!'

Perhaps all I am complaining about is language in the end. We call Caron Keating brave because she died. We call Lance Armstrong brave because he fought – and won. She didn't deserve to die, we want to say. But in saying that, we also admit that he *did* deserve to win. Sometimes it's not about choices.

My fingernails are still a real mess. Tats has taken to coating them with lacquer, which hardens and protects them fantastically. The groove on my right thumb has become a deep crack, and the once-smooth edge is now crenulated. The other day I was pushing out some ice cubes into a G & T for Tatty and I just watched the nail break in two, along the dotted line as it were, while still remaining attached to my hand.

More worrying are my toenails, especially my big ones. There's a semicircle at the base of each where the old nail seems to have vanished. The new nail growth beneath seems hard enough, but yesterday I picked at my left one and nearly took the whole thing off. I'm determinedly walking round the house and outdoors with shoes on as a result: not my first choice in the summer, but I'm terrified of catching them on a chair leg and having to go to A & E.

Thursday 10 August

I am a poet but I have no poem to write, as Heaney says somewhere. I have a book out in the world, but no profile to promote because I am ill. I haven't written anything since last November and have no lines pulling through my mind to begin anything new with. If something does come, it doesn't settle, always one of the first tests of whether anything is worth pursuing.

And then this happens.

My great fear is that, with my last real burst of writing now two years ago – I spent most of last year tidying up, shaping and editing – I have nothing left in the tank. I know what the answer is, of course: 'If you want to write, write!' You have to start splurging again, at some point, to make anything happen, I know that. Somewhere I have a draft of the beginning of a poem called 'Speaking in Tongues', which, as soon as I started it, I sensed could be the title poem of a new collection, something I've never felt before so early on in the process. It seems to me that if I am to take my own advice about going for it and living life to the full, I will have to begin again at some point, and it may as well be soon.

Jack's moustache is really coming on. My top lip is darker than his, but his handlebars are stronger – more defined – than mine. Let battle commence!

Friday 11 August

Today to Lindisfarne, on Holy Island, and then to Bamburgh beach. It meant getting up at seven in order to leave by 8.15, so we could catch the tides. Tilly, aged 3, kept asking where the ponies were. She thought we were going to 'Linda's Farm'.

A good drive up the border, the rolling agricultural land from Kelso onwards looking especially lovely. Not the sunniest of days – by late afternoon, the time we got to Bamburgh, it was distinctly grey – but good banter and humour by all. I walked from the car park to the castle with Shimi. He managed to tell me, in the time it took to get there, the entire plots of the last three Simpsons shows he had watched. He described it very cinematically, that is, paying attention to what was said exactly and to how these lines moved on the plot and character development – though he would not describe it in these terms.

Much laughter in the castle dining room with Paul. I was

having a quiet breather on one of the chairs in the corner when a man came up to me and, looking up from his guide book, asked if 'they really did eat in here?' The thing is, Paul had just been telling me that if I sat there long enough some-one would eventually ask me a question. It reminded me of the time my father was stopped in John Lewis and asked where the haberdashery department was, merely because he was wearing a blazer and tie. All I could think of to say was a rather bland 'Apparently, yes.' But I must have said it author-itatively enough, for he turned away instantly and went on his way, apparently satisfied.

We had a late lunch in the dunes above the beach at Bam-burgh. It was blowing a gale and sand skittered across the sur-face of everything, finding its way into every mouthful. The breakers were truly impressive, wild, white and relentless. The beach was empty, the massive castle glowering over it.

Paul, Jack and I and the boys set up a game of cricket, but the boys soon lost interest. Donning their togs, they raced into the freezing ocean and proceeded to spend the best part of the next half hour dodging and riding the waves. Jack joined them, and, briefly, Tatty.

'I don't believe we're doing this,' I shouted to Jack through the wind, as we staggered up the dunes to find a sheltered spot for our picnic. 'We may as well, now we're here,' he grinned. I couldn't help feeling he was right. Sometimes you just do daft things. I bet it's what we'll talk about five years from now. 'Five years from now': what a fine phrase that is. It's days like today which make you grateful – and greedy – for more.

A lovely luminous drive back from the airport with Tatty after dropping off Bendy on Tuesday. There didn't seem to be the need for rushing all of a sudden, the A7 twilight at once local and timeless, in Seamus Heaney's phrase.

We put on an old Barry White tape – I still say 'tape', even when I mean 'CD' – and talked barehandedly about our love for each other, our children and how proud we were of them.

I confessed to the thought that I considered them to be the main achievement of my life so far.

Monday 14 August

Bendy back in the house. Tats and I drove to the airport to get her last night. Security everywhere. You can't take a sausage on to the plane, now, without it being removed. At the foot of the escalators up to the departure lounge lay a shallow cardboard box. It was filled with biros and cigarette lighters, the new weapons of mass destruction.

We saw her standing on the other side of two sets of sliding doors, in her blue Flybe sleeveless vest, looking tired and sunburned, now a teenager. I signed the document, showed the man my driving licence, and she was ours again. A slight lean of the head, into my kiss, so I catch the top of her forehead. 'I had a wicked time,' she said, without smiling. 'Your moustache is well dodgy.'

Tats has gone into town to Boots to get her 'Children's fight sequence' of photographs developed. I feel I am fast becoming the luddite in the family, listening to myself explaining to guests: 'It's really incredible you know, you just take in your disc, you know, out of your camera, leave it with them, then come back in three days for your shots.' They look at me blankly for a minute, trying to gauge if I am stupid or trying to be ironic. 'Yes,' they say, 'we've been doing it for a year now.'

It's the first time I can remember getting photos back while we are still on holiday. The key word here, of course, is 'remember'. A good article in the weekend *Guardian* by Tim de Lisle outlining how photographs not only aid memory, but over time actually become or even replace, the thing or event remembered. Thus: we get the photos back while still being 'away' and already talk about 'the day the kids fought on the grass and Tatty photographed them' as though it had already passed into family legend, the act of photography both preserver and event in its own right.

What you remember is very unreliable of course. This was made clear to us the week before we came away, when we saw Mummy and Daddy in Exeter, with Marie-Claude and Claude, on a long detour back from the Lakes. As always happens with Daddy, a packet of photographs was passed around, including the family shots of Granny's 100th birthday weekend in Lymington. They were just over a month old. What we all said, on looking at me, bald and very pale, was how terrible I looked. The thing was, during the weekend itself, I spent a lot of the time saying thank you to everyone who said how well I looked. Here was evidence that I looked completely exhausted, overweight and strained.

Tuesday 15 August

Yesterday we went up into the woods above the house and cooked sausages, sweetcorn and potatoes over a fire. Marshmallows for pudding which we ate first; juice and beer and ketchup. We spent hours up there, the kids flying off to add to the two dens either side of the fire-circle. We came back stiff from squatting on logs and reeking of smoke. I took the best part of a roll of film – they all said, 'Oh, it's film', as though I'd just got out a square wheel – as I did with the boat ceremony five years ago, almost to persuade myself that holidays can really be this magical, and relaxed.

Everyone on good form. Paul and I drove Nell and Patrick into town last evening to catch the bus to Edinburgh, then went onto Morrison's to buy ingredients for Ant's Big Curry Evening. It was the first time I'd really cooked properly on a grand scale for a while. It was exhausting, but also uplifting. As if reprising my former life I drank beer in small glasses while Paul acted as sous-chef, secretly topping me up.

The curry was a success – a bastardised version of the Jalfrezi – but the beer was a disaster. I was hung-over, on three small glasses, before we had even finished eating. I may as well accept it: for the foreseeable future I will have to live without drink.

We topped the evening off with an increasingly absurd game of Ex Libris, in which Jack thrashed the rest of us. Useless to try and repeat the jokes – you had to be there. The best material was a Dick Francis novel and *Pilgrim's Progress*. Quietly chuffed to have guessed the right opening to V. S. Naipaul's *A Bend in The River*, never having read it.

Later

At the airport the other night I put into practice John Sutherland's advice in the *Guardian* from his recent *How to Read a Novel*. To tell whether we are going to enjoy a book or not, don't read the opening paragraph but page 69. If you like it there's a good chance you'll like the rest. I tried it out with the new Rachel Cusk, which I loved; the new John O'Farrell, which seemed utterly lazy; the new Maggie O'Farrell, which seemed too much like writing, to use Elmore Leonard's phrase; and *A Prayer for Owen Meaney*, whose tone and voice I adored, without understanding a word. Then I tried the nearest slab of airport bestseller which just sent me to cliché-induced sleep. Apparently you can only buy a book to take onto the plane with you once you've passed through security. I wonder if it's wall to wall Jodi Picoult through there, or if there's a few Cusk-like bits of gold glinting in the muck.

A piece in yesterday's *Guardian* about breast cancer by Dina Rabinovitch, someone, I'm ashamed to say, I've never heard of. She is in New York, feeling hot, having a hickman line fitted to ease intravenous administration of experimental drugs and starting treatment with a new doctor. She admits to waiting three years before coming forward to talk about the lump. She describes with great precision the look of heartbreak – and disappointment – on the doctor's face as she says this: 'I am still amazed they care.'

The book this comes from isn't out till March next year, by which time . . . who knows? . . . I should be well again, about to have a second three-monthly check up, at a guess. About to celebrate being 43, all things being equal. (We should have a party, at the very least to wave off being 42, which has been lousy.) About to finish my novel? About to get a contract? About to complete what I set out to do? Do it today, don't wait around.

Rabinovitch's writing is classy: you can't help but be charmed. I look forward to seeing her story in print – and to reading of her survival while enjoying my own.

Radiotherapy

16 August

The moustache is really coming on.

I began it partly in jest, partly to see if Jack would come with me. Behind all of this was a dare to myself that I would actually follow it through. Tats has said to friends it's to celebrate having hair again: and I have heard myself say 'It's for Al and Dude's party in September' (actually a month away). Whatever. I suspect the real reason is Shimi's chiding: 'I bet you won't do it, Dad. You never do what you say you're going to do.' So, to prove him wrong, I've not shaved for eight days or so.

In town for lunch today with Jack and Jena at the Drum café (a second-hand Jennifer Johnston for £2.50 – I don't need to read p. 69 to know that she is a genius). Jack asked Jena to walk between us so the citizens of Hawick wouldn't think we were an item.

Jack's 'tache makes him look like a *Dodgeball*-era Ben Stiller. The person I most closely resemble is Welsh poet Steven Knight – not famous, but at least he uses the language properly.

Back in Exeter at half-eleven last night; to the Oncology department this afternoon for a 'verification appointment'. This began with a twenty-five minute session on an X-ray table under a large periscope-like device, with three women drawing lines on my tummy in thick felt tip. The positioning of these is crucial. I have to lie in exactly the same position for each of my twenty radiotherapy visits, so they had to get it right today. I asked, in the name of comfort, if I could have a triangular cushion for the space under my knees, as with the PET scan.

I am already dreading it.

Not the pain – of which there isn't any – but the relentless mechanised atmosphere of the place, so different from the warmth across the corridor in Haematology.

That's not to say the radiologists clucking round me today weren't nice ('7.6 across and 1.2 down – is that OK?' one said above me) or attentive, just that I feel I am now on a conveyor belt of care, far from home.

Saturday 19 August

This was made most clear to me by the reactions to my questions about possible kidney damage. Every person I have mentioned it to blinks back at me wordlessly. For me it has been the only question I really want answering – will I come out of this with kidney damage? – but it is as though that part of my conversation with Dr Perry has not reached their notes. 'I'll go and have a look for you,' they smile, kindly, without knowing what I am on about. At last one of them comes back – was it on the notes, or a computer screen? – and says that my kidney is not in the field. My turn to look back blankly. 'It means it won't be radiated, no. Of course, we can't absolutely guarantee that because it's an organ and organs move around. But no, it should be fine. Is that all?'

I miss Felicity's twinkle and Karl being rude. Just before going out I phoned up Ian, who is in charge of my stem cell collection. They are moving it to November now, as I can't be radiated and have bone marrow collected at the same time. 'Hello Ian, it's Anthony.' He knew who I was straight away.

The scary thing about the Oncology dept is that everyone is obviously really ill. They are in Haematology, too, but, apart from the hair loss, don't look it – except Geraldine, who looked iller and thinner each week. Everything there is on the inside. In Oncology, you see a man whose face looks like it is melting, layer by layer. Or a woman with a red, almost purple, neck, swathed in bandages. People in wheelchairs with no hair, in hospital gowns.

Perhaps for this reason, in Oncology, they use the telly. In Haematology I only saw it on once, during the World Cup, the day I had my hickman line out, and the only people I saw watching it were doctors. (In fact, I'm sure I saw Karl shouting at a nurse to move Geraldine's armchair left a bit so he could watch the game from behind the desk.) In Oncology it's on all the time: *Flog It!* followed by *Diagnosis Murder*, appropriate for a hospital waiting area, somehow. You think you're ill, but you could be having treatment from Dick Van Dyke, and his son, Barry.

Some really shitty news yesterday, not in the pile of post-holiday mail, but buried in the avalanche of email, just as I was beginning to wane from wading through it all.

A man I tutored on the Arvon course last year has committed suicide. He was Australian, a retired sociology professor who came on the course on a whim. Someone had dropped out and at the last minute he filled it. He was on a grand tour of Europe, visiting ancestral sites, the trip of a lifetime. He said he hoped Arvon would change his life: his last email, in October last year, said that it was still too early to say if it had, though he had continued writing.

I got the news from Jean, who had forwarded it from Alan, another participant. Andrew was such a lovely man. He was always the one, in our workshops, who would lob in a depth charge of a comment, right at the end of a discussion of a poem, which would have us either speechless with laughter or in amazement at its wisdom. His poems ranged from left-field extemporisation to straight-under-the-fingernails lyrics which it seemed he had waited his whole life to write. I remember clearly telling him to locate that voice and do his damndest to hold onto it, because it was compelling. Even that, though, wasn't enough. It turns out his wife had recently left him and that he had fallen into despair. He left this, one of the last poems Alan had received from him:

Listening

While her mother is far away
the child we never had
is sitting up with me
in the firelight, listening.

It is way past your bedtime.
Don't you love the sound
of the frogs?

More poignant poetry, left on the fridge door:

If all of you said
        ready to go to sleep
but never did

so please do cry
yet use your will
to fast through
        the sad bitter trudge
away from the void

A revelation about poetry day today as I lay in the bath
admiring my luxuriantly hairy arms and thighs (previously
blond): that, having escaped the ultimate rejection slip of
death, the whole business of writing new poems will come,
eventually, but in the meantime, I feel I couldn't care less.
This new – and shocking – feeling of indifference came to me
as I flicked through the new edition of a poetry magazine in
the mail-pile yesterday morning. I could almost feel it creeping up my arms: So what? And this, despite the fact that I
spotted the names of friends and acquaintances, including a
tutee from last year's Arvon in the index. Exactly the same
sensation occurred – it wasn't a feeling, it was a physical
reaction – as I looked at the programme notes to the poetry
festival I read at four years ago. An impeccable array of poets,
workshops, readings and talks. I felt it bounce off me, the
need to compete and say, in the words of the old actor/

light bulb joke, 'That could have been me up there' completely absent. Cancer nearly killed my immune system; instead it seems to have nuked my literary ambition, a proper miracle.

Monday 21 August

First radiation in the bag.

The verification people on Friday were right: it takes about a quarter of an hour, 10 minutes of which is spent making sure you are in the right position, and the rest positioning the machine and then firing the rays. The latter takes 20 seconds, twice.

You lie down on the slab, under the periscope/hairdryer. They press a TV remote control and you move upwards, till you are about shoulder height with them, a foot and a half below the eye of the machine. Lots of clicking again and calling out of numbers. Out come the felt tips. One of them squidges your tummy, pulling one side down a bit while pushing the other up towards your ribs. Another moves your feet five centimetres to the right. So it goes on.

Then, with an invisible nod to each other, they appear satisfied – and vanish.

The lights go off for a second. You become aware of lines of red light criss-crossing the room. One of these is coming from a slit in the ceiling above you. You notice a yellow sticker next to it telling you not to look into the light. You look away and try to banish thoughts of James Bond films. You become aware that Radio 2 is playing in the corner of the room. The lights come on again.

Then there is a buzzing sound and a click.

Your big toe goes all fuzzy.

The radiologists reappear, chatting. They ask you to keep lying still, while explaining that the hairdryer is now going to swivel to a position underneath the small of your back. Out comes the TV remote control.

You try not to think of *Dr Who*.

They smile.

Then vanish again saying I will feel nothing.

And suddenly they're back, saying you can climb off now Mr Wilson and see you tomorrow.

On the way out I noticed that the handrail that runs both sides down the corridor from the waiting area to the radiation room is completely plastered with Thank You cards, stuck on with sellotape. Many depict flowers and sunsets: most are a bit yellowing. It struck me very hard that so many have obviously forged bonds here – and which so far have eluded me.

On the way in, a young porter/male nurse walked me down the corridor, routinely checking my name, date of birth and address before asking me to wait. Then he said: 'And how are we feeling today?' It was the first time I've been asked that question since crossing the corridor. I could have cried.

Tuesday 22 August

'It's a fight every day': new slogan for a spot-removing cream from an ad on telly last night. If proof were needed that war metaphor has seeped into all aspects of language about health, surely it has arrived with this. Below the surface, as with all advertising, is the premise that you can't do without it; and underneath that lies the fear that life isn't worth living if you don't buy what it tells you to.

Tatty came to bed late last night. She'd been on the internet all evening, having read Glenn's email on Lisa's CT scan, looking up lung cancer. We drove out with Sally to Cheriton Fitzpaine to see them this morning. It doesn't look good.

Most people who get it die within five years of diagnosis. The most common killer of all cancers, it receives the least funding on account of smoking. On the Roy Castle site it even says words to the effect of 'If you don't want to know the score, look away now.'

Amazingly Glenn and Lisa were very calm. I think they

realised something was up a few weeks back, when the anti-biotics proved useless and when the first conversation at the hospital was with a consultant. 'It's called "gradual disclosure",' I said, sounding like a know-all. Into the space that followed this remark I wanted to pour my hard-won knowledge of the cancer sufferer, but nothing came. Even when you have lived with the possibility of death for seven months, it still hits you harder when it happens to someone else. I noticed as we sat cradling coffee cups in Lisa's kitchen that the only person who didn't use the word 'cancer' was me.

We all went into their drawing room and said prayers for them.

Their house is fantastically peaceful – with its art and rugs and inglenook fireplaces – as are they. 'Whatever it is,' Glenn said, 'we're OK with it and we'll face it.'

I can't express how courageous I found this. I certainly don't remember feeling the same back in February, whatever anyone told us at the time.

Perhaps there are two kinds of cancer; the one you imagine in the abstract, and the real one you contract, out of the blue. They are both terrifying, but you only know your reaction to the latter when you're actually given the news. I'd bet with most people it isn't what they expect.

Wednesday 23 August

Before my treatment, as we walked down the corridor, the senior nurse told me she had had a bad day. (I don't know her name, she hasn't introdueced herself yet.) 'That's why I'm asking you to take that chewing gum out.' Suddenly I was back at infants school. 'We don't want you choking, do we?'

Later

Tats and I strolled into town for a Wagamama's lunch, leaving the kids to fend for themselves. It rained.

When we got back Tats said we should honour our agreement to go down to the FORCE (cancer) centre on the corner of the main road by the hospital. We introduced ourselves by saying that my neighbour (Lucinda) had recommended we came, and that until now I'd not been well enough, really, to put in an appearance. They welcomed us like long lost friends.

We were sat down on some very comfortable bamboo armchairs. There were pot plants; a Celtic harp CD played in the background. A silver-haired lady brought us tea and a plate of biscuits.

Our introductory interview was with Brenda, who told us she is filling in for Robert, who is on holiday. 'I just pop in from time to time,' she said. Between questions she casually informed us she was responsible for setting the whole thing up. 'A few years ago it was just a space on Cherrybrook Ward, and now look at us.' She got up to fetch us some leaflets.

When she came back she handed them out to Tatty, including the one on 'Cancer for Men.' She turned to me and, smiling, said something which completely floored me: 'You look a million dollars. I'm so pleased you came.' She went away to find more leaflets for us. I rubbed at my eyes and tried to focus on the greenery through the patio door. As Tatty used to say when I was in diagnosis limbo, 'It's only difficult when people are nice.'

Over lunch Tatty looked straight at me and said 'If you had to face mortality again would your reaction be the same?' 'I don't know,' I said, lying. Then I said: 'I'd be more accepting of it.'

'The idea of missing out on seeing what the kids become?'
'Exactly.'
'And what you'd become?'
'What?'
'Well, if it was me, who was going to die I mean.'
'I misunderstood you. I thought you meant me.'
'I meant both of us.'

'I'd be really worried if it was you. I think you do a much better job with the kids than I do.'

A text from Jasper Hampson re my moustache, which he hasn't seen yet. 'Jimmy Edwards, Jimmy Greaves or Jimmy Hill?' he asks. 'None,' I text back. 'It's more gay biker.'

Thursday 24 August

I can feel the tiredness coming back in like a tide. The soreness in my knees has returned: and my legs feel simultaneously leaden and watery.

It's another cool, blowy day. As the Greenbelt weekend approaches I find have very mixed feelings. Excitement at the prospect of reading to an audience again; but dread at telling people I haven't seen for six years that I've been ill.

They called the other night to ask me to introduce – as I know him – Michael Symmons Roberts. I said I'd be honoured. The last time I saw him in fact was the last year I ran the literature programme – its first at the Cheltenham racecourse. I had him reading with his sister-in-law, novelist Catherine Fox. They had never read together before. They put us on on the third floor at the grandstand in a room with windows which wouldn't open. They had arranged the room so that where the lifts opened was just behind the space where the readers stood facing the audience. Their whole reading was peppered with the shouts and laughter of eight and nine-year-old boys running out of the lifts and back in again, in a prolonged game of chase. Not my best moment as a promoter of literature.

Lisa and Glenn get more scan results today. Still no news. I don't think that means it's good.

Tuesday 29 August

Lisa had her biopsy today.

They have found two lumps, masses I should say, one on each lung. While she's under they'll also drain the fluid: she only has 50% capacity at the moment.

Last Wednesday they walked her round the bronchial cancer unit. While she has not been formally diagnosed yet, this is not something you do if you only suspect a chest infection.

Then they told her it was going to be a case of prolonging life rather than looking for a cure. If the word 'unfair' was ever appropriate – and I think it should apply to everyone – it would seem to be more so for Lisa than for anyone else I can think of. Lisa, who is so quietly spoken and shy. Lisa who eats organic food and steers clear of dairy and wheat products. Lisa, who has never gone near a cigarette in her life.

Over the weekend, at Greenbelt we caught up with people we hadn't seen for six years as well as those we'd stayed in touch with so knew about my cancer.

In the former group was Matt Pascoe, who I used to run the literature programme with. He hasn't changed. Still beardy, still saying Fuck a lot, still gloomy about Spurs.

It turns out he's been ordained. It's not his day job ('I'd go mad if I did that') but he works, 'helps out', he calls it, as a non-stipendiary minister in North London, explaining art and spirituality and talking to people who hate church about church.

He had heard about the cancer, from Cameron and Simone. It also turns out he's developed a theology of bad luck. 'You having cancer didn't mean "God says this" or "God thinks you need to learn this", Anthony, it is just bad luck. Shit happens.' This especially pleased Tatty for whom this has become something of a mantra this year.

On Sunday I introduced Michael Symmons Roberts at his reading. He is now at that very special stage of his career where his success, the fantastic quality and depth of his writing, is actually in keeping with the buzz around his name – the prizes, the commissions, the reviews, the websites.

He read exclusively from *Corpus*, saving the first three books for his 'Nightcap' reading in the bookshop. Listening to him I learned again what an absolutely top-drawer piece of work it is. It deserved to win the Whitbread but should have won more. Two things: the high-level sustaining of an enquiry into a particular image or metaphor (in this case, the body); then the completely unforced way that this becomes emblematic of much wider concerns: science/genetics, spirituality/resurrection/miracle.

What he also did so well was give a generous insight into his own writing process. Quoting Don Paterson (or it could have been John Burnside?) he said: 'If you think you have an idea for a poem, kill it instantly. For a poem to work, you see, you need to marry your feeling about something with language or history or some other external source. That then takes you into territory you weren't expecting to work in and the record of this becomes the poem. Otherwise you're just writing what you already know, which kills the poetry.' It was an exemplary reading, so good it made me feel like giving up.

Yesterday, Bank Holiday Monday, the Oncology car park was empty. In early for my only morning visit of the regime, I got chatting to Mark, a shaven-headed man who told me he was a GP with a stage 4 brain tumour.

'They're trialling this new miracle drug on me,' he said. 'My life chances have soared from 4 to 24%. Amazing.'

He asked me if I minded saying what I was in for.

'Non-Hodgkin's lymphoma.'

'Oh NHL. You'll be fine. It's HL – Hodgkin's – you want to avoid.' He lowered his voice and leaned into me. 'Killer. Still,' he said, resuming his normal volume, 'NHL's quite benign.'

I wanted to say 'Not for Dave it isn't. He relapsed. Nor Geraldine.' Instead I just smiled.

'You know the worst thing?' He didn't stop to hear me say 'No, what?'

'The telly.' He nodded at the screen. '*Flog It!*'s on when I normally come. So *depressing*.'

At which point they called my name.

We shook hands again.

'Best of luck.'

'Best of luck.'

We sounded like pilots from Bomber Command, off to give Jerry hell.

Matt said to me at a party at the festival: 'By the way, the 'tache. I mean, it's *great*, but we're all asking each other: '*Why?*'

Today it came off. I had finally found it too irritating.

Tatty says I look very much younger.

As we walked into the chamber for today's session Joanna, the radiologist who speaks to me, said 'To be perfectly honest, I think she's right.'

Friday 1 September

A lovely early September day, a bit of bite still left in the sunshine.

On Wednesday we went in to see Lisa after her biopsy op. She had a drain on her lung, running away into a jug under her bed. Tatty wasn't joking when she said it was the colour of a raspberry smoothie. There seemed to be gallons of it.

She was on a three-bed ward, tucked away, in the thoracic unit on Level 2. The other patients in the room were elderly and watched television, half-asleep. She was smiley but looked winded, yellow. She was still a bit sick from the morphine, she said.

Glenn was there, and the girls. I put my arm round him and he said he had lost it on the phone earlier to his mother-in-law. 'I'm not coping.' I don't really know how to say this, but

I took this as a good sign. It's only when you let go of your own desire and need to stay in control that you really find out who your friends are.

She went home last night.

They get the biopsy results on Tuesday.

On Wednesday evening, before popping in on Lisa, we went for our first massage at the FORCE centre. I admit it, I had been sceptical, even up to the point where Caz asked me to strip to my underpants and put on an ambient piano CD.

Damascene would be to overstate reaction, but let's just say that if I were rich enough I would pay for Caz and her friends to come and massage me and my family every day for the rest of our lives. Why isn't it on the NHS? Don't get me started.

Afterwards, on the bamboo armchairs, we made another appointment then chatted to a woman called Emma, who seemed to want us to carry on talking, even though she was about to lock up for the night. We mentioned Lisa in passing; she said they had been in yesterday afternoon. Then for some reason, as in our conversation with Brenda last week, I had the most urgent need to cry. I don't know what it is about the FORCE centre: whether it's the building, the laying on of hands, or just the way they let you take your time when you're describing your cancer and its effects, but it completely knocks me for six. Can this be on the NHS, too, please, Mr God?

Cancer screws with your memory as well, I'm sure of it. Earlier, after lunch, Tats was doing the *Guardian* quick crossword.

'The best words in the best order,' she said.

'Coleridge,' I said.

'Doesn't fit. Six letters.'

'Shelley then.'

'That's seven.'

'Blank, blank, blank, e, blank, r, blank.'

'Give up.'

'You're going to kill yourself. It's 'Poetry'.'

Yesterday, waiting for the buzzing sound of the radiation machine to start, and having described the return of my diarrhoea, I'm sure I heard Irene Cara singing 'What a Feeling' on the radio in the corner.

Saturday 2 September

10 am. At the kitchen table, alone. Shimi back later from his holiday in Cornwall with Maura, Spencer and Louis. Tatty and Bendy still asleep.

I woke to the doorbell ringing. It was the postman, dropping in the parcel of poems from the Tonbridge Poetry Competition, which I am judging. Haven't looked at them yet.

Went back to bed and lay there pretending to sleep and that I didn't have a raging headache. (I've noticed a large increase of the latter recently – don't know if it's connected to being irradiated. Perhaps I should ask.)

A dull, blowy day, splinters of rain at the window. Not the kind of Indian summer Devon specialises in.

As I lay awake in bed I thought back to talking to Emma at the FORCE centre the other night and why I seem to need to cry when I go there. It's not as if I've kept quiet about my cancer, or hidden myself away – more than I've needed to at any rate. I feel like I've talked to anyone who would listen, whether they have wanted to or not, about little else. But it struck me today: perhaps I haven't really talked about it yet, not properly, not how it's affected me deep down. The verbal form of this crosses my mind not in terms of 'why?' but 'how?', as in 'How on earth did we get here?'

Have started to flick through my Macmillan Cancer-Relief-published *Men and Cancer* booklet. In amongst the facts and figures (NHL is no. 7 in the men's cancer chart, with 4% – 5,504 cases/year and no. 6 for women with 3% – 4,377 cases/year) and the useful glossary, the real gems are the bits in bold type, which are quotes from real living people:

> I am more aware of life now. I seem to be noticing and enjoying things that were always there but that I took for granted before.

I think this pretty much sums it up.

But here is an interesting one, from a 'health professional':

> On the whole, men are very good at finding out in more depth about things like what is known about their particular cancer or what a treatment involves. They also tend to confront the cancer in a more aggressive way, looking on it as the 'enemy'. They may prepare themselves to fight cancer by taking extra care of their general health.

Now I know why everyone – my doctors, friends, colleagues – look so surprised when I tell them I only ever visited one website on lymphoma. I am no John Diamond, genning up to become the world's expert on what I suddenly have. I also now understand their frowns when I tell them I am not 'fighting' the disease. The booklet doesn't go into God in great detail, but I'm sure if it did there'd be a section on 'Asking God "Why me?"' – I'd fail that test, too.

Sunday 3 September

A slow morning, like life before cancer in fact. Tea and muesli in bed, a shuffle through yesterday's papers.

At the kitchen table now, with the Macmillan Cancer Relief booklet open in front of me.

I find I've only just become inquisitive, for instance, about visualising the size of my tumour. The spark for this was reading a review yesterday of the paperback edition of Alan Bennett's *Untold Stories*. Apparently he was told by his doctor that it was the size of 'An Average Rock Bun', the name he gives his essay on the topic. I have been consistently told that my tumour was 4–5 cm in bulk, 'bulky' being the operative word.

Without ever having got out one of Tatty's plastic school rulers to find out what '4–5 cm in bulk' looks like, I know that I've been cheerily going through the summer describing it as 'about the size of a tennis ball.' This is a lie, told, I'm sure, to make my cancer sound more serious. The truth is, 4–5 cm is more like a large lime, or one of the ripe figs Tatty has just bought from Lidl.

I'm told that, pre-radiotherapy, the tumour had shrunk to 1–2 cm. I've been describing this as 'the size of a kidney bean'. This is a lie, too. Looking at Tatty's ruler in front of me, it's more the size of a conker, albeit a small one.

This is odd. First I go round saying how big it is, then how small, exaggerating on both occasions. Consciously or not, it would appear I needed it to be bigger, then smaller, than it actually was.

'Fear underlies what most people feel about cancer.' This, on p. 17 of the booklet, under the subheading 'Feeling afraid.' It cannot be overstated, the simple and profound truth of this statement. If we began all our discussions about cancer by acknowledging the fact of our fear, it wouldn't be such a difficult, embarrassing, awkward and emotive subject to talk about. Yet we persist in toughing it out, sprinkling our speech with phrases like 'prognosis' and 'staying positive' as though by some strange force of alchemy they will make us feel stronger, more in control.

I think why I found talking to Emma at the FORCE centre so emotional is that she didn't mind when I said I wasn't one of cancer's fighters. I'd been talking about the prospect of getting fit again and 'getting back on the bike.'

I saw her wince.

'Like Lance Armstrong?'

'No, not like him at all, actually. I picked up his book the other day, read two words, and realised it wasn't for me.'

'Oh good,' she said. 'For a moment I thought you were one of those,' she paused, looking for the right word, '*fanatics*.' She smiled. 'That's not our style here at all.'

Wednesday 6 September

It has been confirmed: Lisa has lung cancer. It has spread to the mucous membrane of the lung-lining and it is aggressive. They are not going to treat for a cure. Unless a miracle happens, she won't be making it out of this alive. I can't describe the feeling of numbness this leaves me with.

Talking with a friend about it just now I heard the phrases 'It's so unfair' and 'They're so unprotected.' I took the latter to mean that the family have fewer reserves than the rest of us, living in the sticks as they do, and being so shy. I heard myself reply 'I think we all are, when we get the news.'

Cancer is unfair on all of us. And we are all unprotected. However organic your diet, however pure your lifestyle, Lisa's example teaches us that it can come for you next. Most of all, as Matt Pascoe says, this means absolutely nothing. It is just sheer bloody awful luck. Of course she doesn't deserve it. Shit happens.

A small thing happened yesterday: I felt poetry start to come back to me. As Pascoe said at Greenbelt 'The thing is, if you're a writer, you're always half standing to one side saying to yourself "This is good material."' I hadn't even mentioned the diary. But until yesterday I had effectively given up hope of turning the experience into poetry.

The key to making this seem positive was re-reading Julia Darling's amazing *Sudden Collapses in Public Places*. For once a blurb is accurate. There *should* be a copy in every waiting room in the land.

I'd read it for the first time last year, hot on the heels of Arvon and Brie's recommendation of it at the same. I was struck then by its humour, directness and – for want of a better word – courage: the determination not to let terminal illness swamp what Czeslaw Milosz calls 'good spirits'.

Re-reading it yesterday – straight through, twice – I saw again how much of its sinewy strength is derived from the unforced naturalness of the diction, and the no-nonsense metaphors it employs to describe various qualities, physical or otherwise. Thus, in 'Insomnia', sleep becomes a friend who has fallen out with the speaker. The body becomes an extension to the house; and rumours about her health become films projected onto buildings.

As I read I felt the unmistakable – and unfakable – stirrings of lines and promptings arriving through the cloud of tiredness. I lay on the bed, unable to sleep, jotting down random phrases and images without censoring them. I know this to be the gold standard way in which poems begin. It is chaotic, unplanned and as near to preverbal as it's possible to be while still containing thought in the shape of words. It is also very exciting. It means some sort of other shaping process is about to start happening.

Thursday 7 September

Lying reading Julia Darling yesterday I had two violently strong feelings which should have cancelled each other out but didn't.

These were: that this has been a terrible year. I have cancer. Another close friend has just been diagnosed with terminal cancer. Our best friends' marriage has disintegrated. And: I am inexplicably happy. I have a gorgeous wife and two beautiful children who are starting to show potential in amazing ways, in writing and film and music. I have a new book of poems in the world and a room to write them in. I have found out who my true friends are. I have learned that work isn't everything.

All this in a year I never want to repeat and wouldn't wish on anyone.

Today is warm and sunny. The apples have nearly all dropped from the tree. They soften and brown on the lawn. Wasps gather round cracks in the skins, swollen like lips.

Monday 11 September

Perfect autumn days.

Sun out all weekend, burnished and bronze. Hard to sit indoors without either front or back door open. In the mornings, a slight chill, mist. In the evenings, sun low in the sky, the air hangs heavy, full of dew, creamy almost.

New (old) books of poetry have been arriving: Lee Harwood's *Morning Light* and Julia Darling's *Apology for Absence*. Both of them beautiful, humane, and full of risk, in form, language and subject matter.

I think I need to one-click *Sudden Collapses* and *Apology* for Lisa. Why isn't Julia Darling as famous as John Diamond? She has written two of the best books on cancer you could get your hands on. The answer is that she put it into poetry and poetry doesn't sell. Every waiting room should have one: when I get to be king I shall make this law.

At a party on the weekend the phrase I heard myself parrot most frequently was: 'I'm just starting to feel the side effects now.' I watch them glazing over at the prospect of another full-length, all-warts, descriptions, so reign myself in. I just say: 'Yeah, a bit of tummy trouble, and tiredness, of course. They told me to expect it.' Then they say: 'You look great with hair.' (I've noticed that it's mostly men who say this.)

The truth is, a 'weekend off' from the treatment notwithstanding, I'm steadily feeling worse as the radiotherapy progresses. Leaden legs, breathlessness as I walk the stairs. And now, in spite of my tiredness, broken sleep. I find I lie awake, unable to get comfortable, and worrying, not about Life and Death, but about things I did and said twenty years ago, and over which I have no control. After a few hours tossing and turning I find myself waking up into complete clarity for five minutes, then, just as suddenly, falling asleep again. I wake up exactly one minute before the alarm goes off with the weather, thinking it must be half-four or five. It takes me ten minutes before I can move and go and make tea.

Tuesday 12 September

I met with Perry today.
  He told me three key things:

- that he is not expecting any real change in the size of my tumour as a result of the radiotherapy. The real purpose of the current treatment was precautionary, to 'mop up', as he called it, any strong active cells which might still be present on my lymphoma. He said for radiotherapy to change the size of a tumour was 'highly unusual.'
- That he won't be scanning me until three months after the treatment has finished. This is because it takes three months for it to become clear whether or not the tumour has started to grow again. This means I won't know whether the tumour is behaving itself (i.e. not growing) until late November/early December. And even then I won't know if there is still any residual activity left on it. I will have to hope.
- That at the last (PET) scan in June my tumour 'unfortunately' was 'somewhere in the middle' between zero activity and visible growth. He told me that in order to call a disease cancer the cells need to be over a certain percentage, a threshold if you like.

It all left me feeling rather flat.
  Once again I marvelled at how the policy of gradual disclosure allowed me to be informed only now, as I start to

feel sick and exhausted again, that the expected outcome of radiotherapy was not shrinkage of the tumour. Ditto the line about the percentage of cells needing to be present before it is called cancer. This means after all this there still may be a few rogue cells left (the parallels with terrorism are not facetious), just not enough to say 'I have cancer.' I find this amazing. I may be about to enter the grey area of remission, whilst still living with cancerous cells inside me.

Wednesday 13 September

Mid-morning.

Have just come back from being zapped. 'We're taking photographs of you today,' the young Australian radiographer told me.

I learned afterwards that they have in fact been taking one of these each week. 'Partly it's a legal requirement,' she said. 'Quality assurance. And partly we need to see if we're hitting the right spot.'

Then she explained the reason they don't scan me until three months after the treatment has finished is that 'It takes the body that long to settle down again. We're stirring everything up, pretty much. And also, it (the radiation) goes on working for two weeks after we stop. So we need that space.'

'Hence the tiredness afterwards.'

'Exactly, yes.'

Again, gradual disclosure. And only because I pursued the conversation as I pulled up my trousers. This was the first time that someone had explained that the treatment keeps working inside of me after it is officially over. I suppose I could have looked it up on the internet. (Maybe I should have?) But shouldn't I have heard it sooner than this?

While waiting today I watched nearly an entire episode of *Frasier*. I cursed myself for not having set the video. (I needn't worry: I have four episodes stacked up on the digibox, in anticipation of the kids' full return to school tomorrow.) It made a change from what I usually sit through, Dick Van Dyke hamming it up in a white coat in *Diagnosis Murder*. This must go down as the least appropriate thing to watch in a radiotherapy waiting room – skulduggery in ward 56. Either that, or it's so inappropriate it's inspired, an oblique way of making you think your own situation isn't so bad after all.

Thursday 14 September

'I hated it.'

I was talking to the radiologist as I re-buckled my jeans after treatment about yesterday's TV drama, *Losing It*, staring Martin Clunes as Phil, an advertising exec with testicular cancer. The drama followed him from discovering something 'down there', in bed with his wife, to diagnosis, to the operation (he 'lost it'), right through to radiotherapy then also losing his job.

As portrayals in the culture of cancer go, it was pretty good.

What I liked was this: the way it affected his whole family – 'It's not just your cancer, it's my fucking cancer, too' was the standout line, delivered by a very well acted 'stroppy teenager' daughter. Clunes was also excellent, especially as he grew tireder.

Best of all, I thought, was the wife, the strain of keeping the plates of job, family and cancerous husband spinning finally revealing themselves in private tears outside the bathroom one night – witnessed, of course, by the younger child, aged 6.

For a mainstream midweek TV drama, it got nearly everything right.

What wasn't right (this is what I began my discussion with the radiologist by saying) was that Phil gets told everything pretty quickly. He seems to move from GP to 'specialist' to pre-op hospital gown all within ten minutes. I know they have to compress time because it's a drama, but there was no sense here of time dragging, the aeon it takes to get your pictures back from the chemist telling you whether you have cancer or not.

Also, his ward was incredibly quiet. OK, so he had Dave in the next door bed asking him if he had done 'that Guinness ad with the horses,' but no one else that I could see, no groaning through the night and no obs nurses waking him up every two hours. Give me a break.

And the bit that the radiologist hated? Having got the PET scan scene right ('Put your arms above your head and bring your elbows in so we can fit you through the tube') they got the first radiotherapy treatment all wrong. Again, I know they made him say 'Will it hurt?' and 'Where are you going?' and 'What's that noise?' (when it started buzzing) for dramatic effect, but it wasn't at all realistic: he would have been told all of those things before treatment even commenced.

Not that you *are* told everything every step of the way. I said this to her. She looked surprised and a little worried. I had in mind of course that I've only just been told that they aren't expecting shrinkage of the tumour. Gradual disclosure has its advantages, I suppose. It surely lies behind the decision not to say 'You're done' or to say that you are cured. You can just ease back through different shades of grey until 'normal' life returns. That's their assumption, I'm sure of it. Except I can't see life ever being normal again.

The moment in the drama that cut me in two? When Phil asks how long he'll have 'it' for and the oncologist frowns and says 'Five years'. The look that goes across Phil's face at that moment, then across his wife's – that was completely real, a reaction beyond words.

Friday 15 September

Just back from radiotherapy, my last one. In my card to the radiology team I said 'In the nicest possible way, I hope I don't see you soon.' I wonder if it will go in their corridor of fame.

The radiologist was very apologetic about reacting to *Losing It* in the way she had.

We talked while I undid my jeans, then sat on the table, still talking. I noticed the others had left us alone. I wondered if she'd planned it – 'Just give me five minutes at the start, it's his last one'.

She asked if it raised issues for me. I took a deep breath and tried not to use the phrase gradual disclosure. No point in upsetting them on the last day. I explained how I'd only just discovered the other day that the expected outcome of the radiation was not tumour-shrinkage but cell destruction. 'Clinically, it doesn't change anything. Not now I've been treated, nor the probable outcome. But it does change how I perceive the disease. It must have been written down some-where, but no one actually said it. And in terms of the drama I was surprised they didn't have at least one scene with him sitting by the phone waiting for news. That's all I meant. Otherwise it was great.'

Remission

Sunday 24 September

A stiff, tiring week. Days alternately blowy/rainy and sunny/warm. Legs: no energy in them. Breathless at the tops of stairs. Knees: sore and achy. Sleep: broken, every night. (I wake up, pee, then lie there praying for Lisa to get better). Dreams: the bad ones return – the lecture/seminar/poetry-reading-dream, my briefcase and the auditorium empty, after I arrive late.

Last night, amazingly, I had my first dream about cancer.

It went like this. Karl and I were talking and walking in 'Hospital Road', the main arterial corridor which runs the length of the hospital, from Haematology down to orthopaedics. Quite casually, and as though I already knew, he told me that the radiotherapy hadn't worked and that I would have to have an even stronger course of the same. One so strong, they give it to you through water, in a specially designed swimming pool . . .

I woke up feeling utterly drained, and worried. Karl said over his shoulder: 'The thing is, Anthony, it's a fucking nasty disease and you had it bad. I'm sorry, but we've got to make sure'.

Andy has been round for coffee. He handed me a copy of his fabulous looking new book, *The Fall of the Rebel Angels*.

Lots of gossip here as well – I haven't seen him for ages – but more importantly it was so good to natter about books and writers in that *other* way, enthusiastically.

As he was leaving he told me he'd read my fox poem at Arvon and that it had been received with uproarious laughter. 'But who is it?' they all asked. 'We've never heard of him.'

I discussed how cancer seems to have killed off my ambition with Jean, who visited yesterday. 'Well, yes,' she said, not prepared to concede to me. 'Except we're not ambitious really, are we? Only for the next poem. The rest is meaning-less.' And then she told me a story about a poet who had rung her up to ask her what they should do to get themselves a higher profile.

I tried to explain to her that having the book in the world but not having had a chance to promote it was very try-ing. 'Your time will come,' she insisted. Maybe she knows something I don't. Then I confessed to her I've begun writing poems again and feel tempted to enter the Poetry Business Pamphlet Competition. 'What have I got to lose?' She said people would one day *need* – that was her word – to read both my prose and poetry accounts of having cancer, and that I shouldn't spare myself in choosing one over the other.

On Saturday afternoon we strolled into town to look at Lisa's new textile hangings in the Royal Albert Museum. They are beautiful, unquestionably the real thing. As we mounted the staircase where they hang, I guessed correctly which two were hers and felt smug. A wonderful sudden moment of peace with Tats on the sofas in the gallery looking out onto them, as if cancer were in neither of our lives. One of the hangings is called *All Lives All Dances All is Loud*, which is a line from an old forager song from the area they live in. I can feel a poem coming on.

Monday 25 September

I spoke to Karl today to arrange my stem cell collection. He is back from his rock collecting trip to Iceland, and is full of it. As his house will be, if his description is anything to go by.

He greeted me warmly, immediately making me feel nos-talgic. Nostalgic, for a time when I had cancer and felt shitty? What am I saying? But the truth is that I miss it, the contact and the banter on the ward, the being asked how you are and told you look great even though you know you do not.

Robyn is right. The early part of remission is hard – not

just because you feel wiped from radiotherapy, but because it is lonely. Your visitors dry up. After all, you're not dying any more. The phone stays silent. (Except for your parents.) Thank God for *Frasier* and the internet.

I'm booked in for mid/early November. GCSF injections from the 10th–13th, for three days, for the collection. Usually they get this in one go, he told me, but you never know, so block book the rest of them out.

He asked me how I was and didn't miss a beat when I said knackered. 'Yup, you'll feel that for a while,' he said. 'Probably get worse, you know.'

'Really?'

'Yup, for a while.'

All I could think of was that earlier in the year this is what he went through himself.

A walk into town to revisit Lisa's hangings in the Royal Albert Museum. I sat for over three quarters of an hour looking and listening as people came and went. I filled three pages with phrases and the beginnings of stanzas, and felt like a writer again.

An odd thing in the bath today. A perfect rectangle of denuded hair, in exactly the area they zapped me during radiotherapy, just to the right and centre of my tummy. How did one of the cool young Australians put it when I asked her why I didn't have any sunburn there?

'Let's just say the layers of, er, that you have a few more layers, of, er, fat there, er, than elsewhere on your body.'

Monday 2 October

October already.

A typical Devon weekend, hilarious stairod rain, then sunshine, then grey clouds and winds. There are two apples left on the tree. The path up to the house is a cider-smelling orange quag where the crab apples have been trampled into the gravel.

Last Tuesday was stunning, clear blue sky, sun genuinely warm.

I remember, because I walked by the river for a little way before having to throw the towel in, exhausted. It was both exhilarating (it was too nice to be in the house) and depressing.

Today, after a grey start, is the same. But I won't be going anywhere, except for milk.

It took watching Stephen Fry's programme on telly, about 'the secret life of the manic depressive', for the penny to drop. Not that I suddenly think I'm bipolar, just that what I'm currently going through is the closest to depression I've had during this whole business. I didn't get it with chemotherapy, even though I felt substantially worse; whatever it is with radiotherapy (I always want to say 'radiation') – it certainly seems to have flicked a switch. I wonder if this is what John Diamond meant in his book – he had radio long before chemo and said he got very depressed with it. The irony is, I'm not depressed about having cancer – they think they've sorted that. It's to do with uncertainty, coupled with the fact that I'm feeling lousy but not officially being treated. It is very counter-intuitive. And nobody tells you about it. The tiredness, yes, is mentioned. But not how you *feel.* In a jokey email to a friend last week I said I was 'sick and tired' of it all, ha ha, as a general feeling of queasiness is also a daily fixture (though thankfully, so far, without any actual throwing up). But as phrases go, that pretty much sums it up. Perhaps it is worse, having had a glimpse of almost feeling normal over the summer. Another factor here is that everyone goes round saying how well I look all the time. Given that many people have said this all the way through my treatment, including the 'waxwork' phase of chemotherapy (© the kids), I am tempted to not believe them. But it's true, even to myself. I have hair, colour, eyebrows. But what I want to say is 'If only you knew.' The line of Stephen Fry which brought this home was when he said 'What people don't realise is that on the outside I'm doing

250

what I do, being witty, urbane and charming, but inside my head I'm screaming for it all to end so that I can go back to bed.' Straight after the programme we watched the first in a new series of QI, his new quiz programme/vehicle. It made me laugh out loud. But I also felt for him, knowing what was going on underneath.

I've had enough of 'Fine.'

I am done with cheerful.

This unwelcome new side of the cancer experience is even more ironic given that the last two weeks have been extremely productive. Poems have been arriving, as Raymond Carver says somewhere, every day. (Perhaps this also explains why this is my first diary-visit in a week. I seem incapable of doing both.) But, as the Stephen Fry example shows, depression does not prevent creativity in those who have it, but rather, seems to foster it. No, it's not that I am being creative that I find ironic; it is that through these first forays into putting my experience into poetry I am only just starting to realise what I have been through and how angry I feel about it.

The latter, in particular, has been a revelation. Not that I am angry with any one or thing or experience – just angry. In the poems it comes across as surface annoyance and irritation at what people say to you and how they expect you to be. But I know underlying this – as in the proverbial iceberg analogy – is a vast hidden mass which cannot (and must not) be seen above the surface. Until now, that is.

Buried on p. 30 of yesterday's *Observer*, an article by Karol Sikora, medical director of Cancer-Partners UK and formerly Professor of cancer medicine at Hammersmith.

Entitled 'It's time to take the politics out of cancer' the piece hit me on several levels. (I'll come to the politics bit in a minute.)

Firstly he gives an extremely clear explanation to the lay reader of what is going on when a patient is diagnosed:

We now understand its origins in the intricate molecular control machinery of the cell. This results in essentially a runaway cell with the accelerator on and no brakes. Slowly, the abnormal cell multiplies and spreads to other parts of the body wreaking havoc as it goes.

I wish I'd had this kind of thing to read back in February; though Felicity and Karl's oral explanations said more or less the same thing, there's something so transparent about this which I find bizarrely reassuring.

Secondly, he has no time for what politicians are doing for cancer sufferers as a whole. The 'media frenzy' over Herceptin took hold earlier this year, the Department of Health stepped in 'without waiting for our drug regulators' (NICE) assessment and decided that it should be available for all suitable breast cancer patients. . . . This is crisis management driven by political imperative.' Taken to its extreme, as in Israel a few weeks ago, this results in the kind of behaviour from 'lobbyists' where they go on hunger strike until the decision to make a 'wonder drug' available is brought forward, irrespective of cost.

His third point is that we are now living in an age where we view cancer as a romantic disease. To make this point he refers to Susan Sontag's *Illness as a Metaphor*: the Victorian poets had TB, the Eighties brought HIV/AIDS, and now we have cancer. His question is this – and it's not a comfortable one. Knowing as we do that not all cancers are equal (he cites the example of an old man dying of prostate cancer receiving different treatment from a woman of 40 with breast cancer) is the price we put on treatment – i.e. life – determined by 'the political importance' of the disease, by romanticism or 'robust analysis of [each drug's] cost-effectiveness'? The key phrase here is 'political importance'. Breast cancer, or, specifically, the type treatable with Herceptin, seems very 'hot' just now. But one day, if predictions are correct, it could be NHL. I have an interest in this, because Rituximab is just one such drug or agent on which NICE will soon be deciding to promulgate – or not. At the moment it is not cost-effective to give it to people with indolent NHL. But what if rates of diagnosis of that start to multiply (i.e. it becomes high profile) or someone famous is diagnosed with it? Is it right that they should have it, even if their chances of survival are not necessarily improved by taking it?

The radiotherapy department has just rung to ask how I am. I told them I was feeling increasingly sick and tired (ha ha) the further I went away from the treatment. But I couldn't say I was depressed. I just couldn't. They said to drink lots of water and to call if I needed to talk. It's well-meant advice. But we both know I'm not going to do it.

Tuesday 3 October

A beautiful blue autumn day. Crisp morning air early on and 'plentiful dew' (Jaan Kaplinski).

I wonder how far sensible discussion of cancer will ever be possible in this country. For every Sikora piece there is a Darren Clarke's wife/Kylie's new haircut/Caron Keating biography waiting, like one of Medusa's snakes, to take its place.

The real problem here is that it isn't always these popular figures who are responsible for ensuring that our language seems destined to continue dealing with cancer in a neo-romanticised/idealised way, i.e. talking only of battles, fights and bravery. Last week I watched one of those ads on telly (like the current one for giving blood) which it is hard not to be moved by, by Cancer Research UK. Well shot, beautifully chosen music and graphics. The phrase they chose to leave you with? 'Help us in the battle against cancer.' It seems to me we should distrust this promulgation of war imagery most thoroughly. Either that, or every disease, from HIV/AIDS to the common cold, should become one. I'm not in favour of that either. I think it would lead to a permanent post-Diana-style sob-fest fetishisation of just about everything. But it might be more honest.

As one of the assassins gunned down by Matt Damon in *The Bourne Identity* says 'No one tells you about the headaches.' On top of the queasiness bracketing each day at breakfast and supper, I wake with an absolute shocker, worthy of a good night of Otter at the Hourglass. But no.

Linda Southwood came in for about three minutes yesterday afternoon and left me feeling both puddle-like and less alone. She is ten years into her own (breast) cancer remission now, but remembers the treatment like it was yesterday. 'Chemotherapy made me feel like a princess,' she said. 'During radio I felt like a pork chop.' This ought to go at the front of cancer treatment text books for medical students. I welled up across the kitchen table as she spoke: 'I know they had their sums to do each time, so they didn't cook me, but they could at least have asked how I was. On the last day one of them said they liked my cardie. It cut me open.'

Then she spoke intensely and briefly, about how the early stages of remission – 'No one's looking out for you any more' – were much harder than the bulk of the treatment. She seems to know all about me.

Saturday 7 October

'I don't want to commit suicide. I just wouldn't mind being dead.' The Stephen Fry programme on depression still needles away at me. Not only because it sums up how I felt exactly at this time two years ago, but also because it's a neat summary of how you feel during cancer treatment, on the worst days of chemotherapy and radiotherapy, that is. It's made me think very hard, this latest bout of feeling low – dare I say depression? – about whether there is a connection between radiotherapy and being miserable. John Diamond, if memory serves, freely admitted to being depressed while he had his radio treatment, I wonder if there are any studies on it. In spite of their (three minute) courtesy call to check 'how I was doing' it's the being left on your own to get on with it and gradually feel 'normal' again that I find so difficult.

What do I have? The queasiness and nausea which I get at breakfast and at 5 pm each day at last seem to be easing off. (Remember, I finished radio three weeks ago yesterday.) Touch wood etc.

The rectangle of denuded hair on my tummy looks pinker and barer by the day.

I take ages to drop off to sleep – never a problem before, even during chemo (except in the Bad News phase). And I don't seem to sleep much beyond 5/5.30 any more. I lie there listening to Tatty breathing, feeling dreadful. The good part of this is that in this dreamy just awake state, many lines of poems seem to arrive in the half-light. The bad side is I don't get them down fast enough, or accurately enough, before the day starts.

Monday 9 October

It's a pretty rum state of affairs when it takes having cancer to admit that you sometimes get depressed.

We had Non for the weekend. On Friday evening Tats went out to a farewell dinner of a long-standing member of staff from school, so we watched telly with her upstairs. Somehow we got onto the Stephen Fry programmes. She'd seen one, she said, and would love to see the other. The standout line, the one all the papers quoted in their telly reviews, went something like 'I just have this little voice in my head telling me I'm a useless cunt all the time.'

Whether or not I've been feeling *exactly* that recently I certainly did after hearing Andy read at the Picture House on Saturday, just as I did after hearing Symmons Roberts at Greenbelt. Basically, it's game over. When you look at the variety in the use of forms, the copiousness of the vocabulary, the wit, the learning: it takes your breath away. And hearing them read, they're as light as a feather, charming, all achieving lift-off, while remaining absolutely themselves, demure, clotted, bursting. I can't compete. My wee poems about cancer, my 'How To Pray for the Dying' my 'The Year of Drinking Water' just pale in comparison.

In the Saturday *Guardian*, a moving sequence of photos from Annie Liebovitz, of Susan Sontag. I'll admit I had forgotten that Sontag had died of cancer. There's one shot of her actually receiving chemotherapy – through what looks like a hickman line in her chest. Her eyes are fixed sideways onto the nurse bending in towards her. She's smiling, but not conventionally beaming. It's rueful, accepting, but determined as well. It made me well up as I came across it. She captures exactly that moment of 'fighting the good fight', of defiance mixed in with vulnerability.

Talking with Tats on the weekend I came across another analogy for radiotherapy: Ofsted inspections. They are relatively short (now) and mechanically painless experiences – but the side effects are long lasting and take ages to fully leave the system. As I watch Tatty go through the motions of hoop-jumping each weekday night – just to stand still – I know that we're both enduring the same kind of aftershock.

We've entered a new era with the kids. Shimi came down to breakfast one morning last week, turned off the *Today* programme, and asked if I could find him Radio 1. It was the Chris Moyles Show: ten minutes of meaningless banter followed by the Scissor Sisters. I made their packed lunches through gritted teeth.

Friday 13 October

Poems have been arriving each day all week. But still my spirits do not lift. Bumped into Maura and Spencer yesterday on errands in town and it was everything I could do not to crack open like an egg on the pavement. We went for coffee and gossiped about losing weight and university politics. Felt done in. Went across the road to the Oxfam bookshop and treated myself to books I don't need (e.g. a 1991 copy of *Poetry Review* about American poetry). Also bought (in Waterstones) the new *PR* issue – my first for five or so years. It looks good. And that Jane Kenyon *Selected* which Bloodaxe have brought out. That looks good too. Spending money I don't have.

Tats came home teary last night and Wednesday too. It just reminded me that I felt the same. Did my best to console her, certain I did a poor job. Lay in bed last night talking to the ceiling about how hard it's been post-radio. Someone said to me in the street yesterday 'It [i.e. radio] made my dad depressed too.' So perhaps this is what I *should* feel.

This morning Sally appeared with a huge bunch of lilies and some hot smoked salmon from the deli to say they were thinking of us. 'What with Lisa being so poorly and everything everyone's taken their eye off you for a bit. We want you to know that we know you're not out of the woods yet.'

Felt like cracking open then, too.

I don't know what is stopping me going for counselling. I'll go and pick up the phone now.

Tuesday 16 October

What is it like being told you are in remission from cancer? As when you are diagnosed, it takes a while to sink in. You're not sure you heard it right. You want to drive back to the hospital and say 'Are you *sure*? That it's *me*?'

It's a day not unlike the one eight months and two days ago, when I was first diagnosed. You put the phone down, say 'oh' to yourself and go back to trying to read the paper. You feel a little flat, rather than shell-shocked, in despair. News of remission's much the same. Outside it is raining. As on the day of diagnosis, there is a child at home, watching telly, only this time off school with a cold. You don't feel like punching the air. You maybe do cry a little, but only when you tell people, and they start crying, on the phone. It's a normal day. You feel a little numb. You think, *Did I really come through this? Was it real?* It's still as though it's happening to another person.

It's the news you've longed for, but, you think, maybe I should just check my email.

It's a very grey day.

Tatty and I waited for an hour before Felicity saw us at 11.45. She asked after me, beaming her lovely smile as always.

I explained about the tiredness and she asked if Perry had told me to expect it. I told her he had, but that I'd hoped it would be over by now.

In truth it was I who used the word first. 'I was hoping that it might be easing off now, as I edge remission.'

'You're not edging into it. You're in remission.' She smiled.

'Really?'

'Yes, as far as we're concerned, unless you show signs of the disease coming back, you're better. That's it.'

'Wow. Great. Wow.'

She said they'd scan me in November, as expected, and that, for the first year at any rate, they would see me in clinic every three months. 'But we won't scan you each time. I don't think we'll need to. We don't want to overdo it.'

She examined me very briefly, for lumps.

As I put my shirt back on I told her I'd been feeling a little flat recently. I couldn't bring myself to use the word 'depressed'. Felicity had no qualms. 'Well, we can always get your GP to prescribe some sleeping tablets or a mild anti-depressant.'

I looked at Tatty.

'If it helps,' Felicity said.

Tats read my mind and said 'Let's give it a couple of weeks, see how we go.'

On the way out she found me a leaflet for the Haematology specialist support counsellor. 'Her name's Alex, she's lovely, brilliant, actually. I'm surprised we never told you about her.'

'You probably did but I probably didn't take it in.'

'Well that's it. You're so concerned with what's in front of you that you're just dealing with that.'

'Exactly.'

'And when you think about it, you've been through an enormous amount of stress. And now maybe you're just realising just how much.'

'Exactly.'

'It's not uncommon you know. We worked with a psychiatrist on a project some years ago who found that over 30% of our patients feel depressed after their treatment is over.'

'I'm not surprised.'

'Like you, especially after radiotherapy.'

She handed me the yellow leaflet.

I wanted to say what an outstanding and perceptive doctor she'd been. I wanted to hug her.

Instead, clumsily, I mumbled 'Thanks again for everything.'

It was tipping when we got outside.

Nic has just been on the phone. I said to her, 'Just as you don't fall apart when you're diagnosed, you don't exactly begin popping champagne corks all over the place when the news is reversed.'

Lisa rang as well. She sounded terrible. She hadn't read the email, so I had to tell her. 'Oh Anthony, that's *fantastic* news,' the warmth in her voice tangible. I felt only guilt.

Part of the flatness – nothing to do with rain, nothing to do with tiredness – is knowing that I live while others choose not to. Ellie, who has been typing the first thirty pages of this manuscript out for me, committed suicide yesterday afternoon.

She had a visit from the crisis team earlier that day and

urged them to admit her so that she could begin Lithium treatment ASAP. They declined.

Between the time they left – lunch? – and Philippa returning from work at 5 she must have decided enough was enough.

She was emailing me only last week asking my advice on the pamphlet of poems she's been putting together. I said I'd be delighted to help her – and then didn't, of course. 'Too tired, too busy,' I heard myself say to Tatty. 'It's not your fault,' she said. 'I think she meant it this time. It's nothing to do with what you thought of her poems. She knew you loved them.'

Friday 27 October

I did something previously unimaginable yesterday: I rode my bike. Not my old bike, which got stolen from the garage a couple of weeks ago, but my super-dooper new Marin hybrid with mud guards and a kryptonite lock. I took it for a spin around Fore Street, near the Bike Shed shop, threw the gears on a hill start and felt deeply foolish. There are some things you *can* forget. Second time round it rode like the wind and I said 'I'll take it.' Got a new helmet too, and I know it won't be long before I go back for an Altura Nevis jacket in fetching luminous yellow. As Ruth Picardie says, sometimes retail is the only therapy that will do.

Have just been up to the deli for olives and salami for a sandwich. Who should I bump into but Felicity? We had one of those it's-a-small-world moments as we discussed the fact that her daughter rows with Abigail (Ellie's sister) for the UCL medical school. We discussed Ellie at length. Felicity said she's known several people who've killed themselves, one of them a brilliant oncologist. I described how the crisis team had come round and seen her that day, but obviously decided against admitting her. 'Why can't they do more for these young people?' she said, looking teary.

Then we stood outside in the cold chatting about the ward, and I admitted to her that I've been keeping a journal about the whole thing. She looked teary again. 'You have nothing to worry about, Felicity,' I said, 'You came out of it brilliantly.' Then I asked what Karl's surname was. 'I've written him a poem, you see, er, about blood.'

'He'd love to see it, I'm sure.'

Saying goodbye I thanked her and said again she had nothing to fear. For a split second I toyed with the idea of stooping a little to give her a kiss on the cheek. As a friend. And because I will never stop being grateful to her, not just for her skill but also her great humanity. But no. I crossed the road and she disappeared into the flower shop.

The sun has just popped out, after a heavy shower; the washing line a string of pearls.

It's time to live.